California Dons

Balcony of the General Castro House

John Howell Photo

California

Dons

*Though fiction, this book is carefully based on the
personal recollections of Señor Don Estolano Larios
and deals with Californians of a century ago.*

By

RALPH LeROY MILLIKEN

VALLEY PUBLISHERS
Fresno, California
1967

Lithographed in the United States of America by
SIERRA PRINTING AND LITHOGRAPH COMPANY

INTRODUCTION

THIS BOOK is a result of the visit of an old, old man, Señor Don Estolano Larios, at my home many years ago. Don Estolano had come to make me a visit of two weeks, but he remained as my guest for three and a half years! He occupied himself furnishing me with the material—some four hundred typewritten pages—on which to base the story of his life. We made innumerable visits to San Juan Bautista and the scenes of his boyhood, traveling as far south as Santa Barbara, where he re-lived for several days at the old mission his life as a school boy nearly a century before.

Mr. Larios also translated for me a manuscript now in the Bancroft Library, *"Vida y Adventuras de su Padre, Manuel Larios,"* that he had written in 1878 at the request of his friend, Thomas Savage, for Mr. Bancroft. The manuscript is written in Spanish and depicts the life and adventures of his father, Don Manuel Larios, who started out in life as a private soldier in the army of the King. At his death in 1865 he was the owner of twenty-five thousand acres of land and had risen to the position of leading Don of San Juan Bautista.

This story is thus based for the most part on scenes and events of that era long ago when the Mexicans in California were painfully adjusting themselves to the overlordship of their American neighbors who had poured uninvited into their country.

The aim of this book is to picture life in California as it went merrily on a century ago. History told in story form is always more entertaining than mere lists of dates. Names used have been changed and are fictitious, but most of the accounts and happenings given are true to the knowledge and restatement of my friend, Señor Don Estolano Larios.

The Spanish way of life is now fast disappearing in California. It was an era of great personal bravery. Men, single handed, fought grizzly bears, wild bulls and marauding Indians. Young boys rode bull calves for excitement. Children made pets of grizzly bear cubs.

A new American way of life is taking its place. Now the reckless Spanish brand of personal courage is quite unknown. We are completely pacified, subdued, civilized. We live a soft, easy life; the very kind of life that makes it possible for dictators and their imitators to undermine our very existence.

But it is a pleasure to look back on an era of personal bravery that is gone. Men lived differently in the old day, and perhaps better.

My one regret is that this sprightly young Don of a century ago, who grew up in the days when the West was young, is not still with us and able to enjoy reading "his book."

RALPH LeROY MILLIKEN

Los Banos, California

PREFACE
The Larios—Higuera Families

Estolano was the youngest of thirty-nine children. His father, Senor Don Manuel Larios, began life as a private soldier at the age of 15 and rose to the rank of Lieutenant.

Before the American Occupation of California he succeeded in getting from the Mexican Government not merely one, but two grants of land. One was the "Rancho de San Antonio", adjoining the mission of San Juan Bautista. This rancho was one square league in extent. It consisted of four thousand acres and was three miles square. This was called "Ranchito", meaning the "Little Ranch".

Don Manuel's larger ranch was the "Rancho de Santa Ana & Quien Sabe", eleven square leagues, which he owned in partnership with Don Juan Miguel Anzar, the brother of Padre Anzar, the Franciscan monk in charge of Mission San Juan Bautista. Don Manuel had a family of twenty-two children, nine of whom were living. During the summer months they spent their time at Santa Ana, four leagues east of San Juan, but in the winter when traveling was difficult they lived at the Ranchito adjoining the Mission.

Estolano's mother was Senora Maria Rosario Armas de Higuera y Larios. She was married at an early age to Juan Higuera, a young man who went by the nickname of "Juan

Tambour", meaning Juan the drummer. Juan was such a skillful drummer that he could play the military calls on the snare drum—advance, retreat and other maneuvers. He was always much in demand whenever there was a little rebellion being staged against the Mexican Governor at Monterey. Juan grew up to be a local politician. Eventually he became Mayordomo for Don Juan Miguel Anzar and had his headquarters at Santa Ana along with Don Manuel.

In 1845 when General Jose Castro set out to overthrow Governor Micheltorena, Juan Tambour went south with the army, and in a battle near Los Angeles he was among the few killed. Juan Tambour had a family of sixteen children, seven of whom were living. His widow was a very beautiful woman and after the death of Juan Tambour she became the wife of Don Manuel. The wedding took place in the Mission of San Juan Bautista. Patrick Breen and his wife, of Donner Party fame, stood for them as witnesses. Padre Anzar performed the ceremony. Their one and only child was Estolano.

Often there were as many as fifty people living at one time at the Ranchito. Don Manuel was never so happy as when surrounded with children and grandchildren. And with the Larios family there lived also the children of the Higuera family. It was all one huge, grand family.

The Ranchito was a children's paradise. All the time was playtime. The grandchildren were of all ages and sizes. Although many were older than Estolano, yet he was their uncle—their "Tio"—and according to Spanish family tradition, he was their superior and entitled to their obedience. Estolano was very quick-witted and he was not long in learning how to lord it over his nieces and nephews like a true Spanish Don.

Chapter I

ESTOLANO

"BUT MAMMA," declared the still wide awake little Estolano, "I am *not* going to go to sleep." The tearful little urchin tried to explain."I want to *play* some more!"

Doña Rosario had been endeavoring unsuccessfully for some time that warm spring evening to put the three-year-old baby of the household to sleep. Estolano's little hammock swung from the posts of the wide veranda that extended all along the east side of Don Manuel's *Casa*. This square, two story, thick-walled adobe house served Don Manuel and the numerous members of his household as a fortress as well as a home.

The persistent swaying of the hammock, however, by his patient mother finally conquered the rebellious spirit of this little "fighting Catalonian" and, surrendering at last, Estolano sank into peaceful slumber.

"May it be the angels who awaken thee!" was the parting prayer of Doña Rosario as she took leave of her sleeping son. Walking away quietly toward the *sala* or living room of the house, the tall, active, still beautiful though middle-aged mother caught sound of the eerie wail far in the distance of a coyote barking plaintively in his loneliness. Another howled as if in answer. But Doña Rosario was accustomed to hearing the calls of these slinking animals roaming far and wide over the vast pasture lands of the Santa Ana Rancho and thought nothing of it. She was far more interested in the Santa Ana Peak rising high in the eastern sky. Its towering crag was the one thing that linked her still with her native land. Pausing for a swift glance she recalled for a fleeting moment her girlhood home in the far away Pyrennes.

Sitting proudly astride Regalo, his magnificent chestnut saddle horse, Don Manuel, the owner of the Santa Ana Rancho, only a few weeks before had been making the rounds of his ranch. Unexpectedly he came upon two strange young Indians prowling inside the high adobe walls of his horse corral.

"Vamoose! Get going!" ordered the old Don as he rode boldly into the enclosure.

"You can't boss us!" retorted one of the snoopers defiantly.

Disrespect was something that this old Spanish officer would never tolerate from anyone. Uncoiling his lariat and doubling the strands in his hand, he lashed vindictively at the backs of the retreating Indians, as he sent them bolting out of the corral. The two young rascals, nursing their sore backs, promptly made their way to their native village in the San Joaquin Valley, there to spread the story of their punishment.

This once-populous Indian village stood far over the mountains to the east from the Santa Ana Rancho. The village site is now marked only by a wide stretch of perfectly level ground. The soil, however, is still soaked to the hardness of pavement by the grease from the innumerable horses and bears that have been roasted and eaten there.

On this camp ground a century and more ago a group of primitive, mud-coated human beings were hunched around a tiny camp fire listening to the complaints of the two young men who had been so unceremoniously driven from the Santa Ana Ranch.

"Don Manuel can't whip us like that," whimpered one as he sought to stir up sympathy among the squatting aborigines.

"In the embers of his own *Casa* we will roast Don Manuel

alive!" chanted in gutteral tones first one and then another of the listeners.

Another plotter, more jovial than the rest, nodded in agreement. This warrior was as anxious as the two snoopers themselves to whip up enthusiasm for a raid on Don Manuel's Rancho. But his interests were not in fighting other people's battles, however. His was in good eating.

"Don't forget," this horse-eater urged. "Don Manuel's big adobe corral is filled every night with the sleekest, sweetest tasting horses that anyone could want for roasting and eating."

When the moon is full, they all agreed, an arrow pointing west would be fired into the oak tree on the trail leading to Don Manuel's Rancho. That would be a sign to all other Indians crossing the mountains that a raid was taking place on the Spanish settlements.

"As we gradually encircle Don Manuel's *Casa,*" suggested a veteran of many raids on Don Manuel's establishment, "let's all bark like coyotes." And the wily old raider laughed heartily. "No one in the *Casa* will suspect that it is us who are encircling the Rancho. We'll fool Don Manuel completely. He will think we are merely a bunch of coyotes howling in the dark around his house and will pay no attention until it is too late."

Doña Rosario gave a last lingering glance at the sharp crag of Santa Ana Peak. "If only I could visit my native land once more!" sighed the lonely woman. Then tip-toeing softly she left the veranda and entered the living room. Already Martina, the favorite daughter of Don Manuel and the bride of fun-loving Melicio, had the shutters at the windows securely fastened for the night and was lighting the evening candles. These tallow lights in their sconces fastened along the wall were feebly chasing the darkness into the remote corners of the large, rudely furnished living room.

"Don't you think, Martina," asked Doña Rosario anxiously,

"that there are an unusual number of coyotes barking around the house tonight?"

Martina listened carefully, then finally answered her step-mother, unalarmed:

"Oh, I don't know, mother. Melicio told me the vaqueros butchered sixty head of cattle today. Uncle Justo is coming tomorrow, you know, to make jerky and candles for the year. Probably this torrent of fresh blood is what is attracting all the coyotes in the country this evening."

Doña Rosario, still uneasy, made her way to the out-door bake ovens a few yards from the house, where several women and girls of the household were still busy in the evening twilight baking bread to be taken by the family to Mission San Juan Bautista for Holy Week.

Mary Arroyo, a young girl from the neighboring ranch of Cruz Cervantes, happened to be at the Santa Ana at the time helping with the baking.

"Well, Mary," asked Doña Rosario, "how is your father getting along with his knee?"

"Quite nicely," answered the girl politely. "Of course he will never be able to walk very well again. The bear bit his knee cap clear off." Then, tempted irresistibly, she added: "As father lay there bleeding and helpless on the ground he could hear the crunching noise of the bear's jaws as the wicked animal devoured father's knee cap. Father felt he was being eaten alive."

"How terrible!" shuddered Doña Rosario.

Don Manuel, who always retired "with the chickens" was already safe in bed and sound asleep.

The *Casa* or ranch house of Don Manuel was built as strong as a fortress. Indeed it was a fortress, for Don Manuel and his partner, Don Juan Miguel Anzar, had been given the Santa Ana Grant of fifty thousand acres of land partly on the agreement that the Santa Ana would be maintained as a bulwark against the incursions of marauding Indians from the San Joaquin Valley. Of late years these Indians had been making more and more horse-stealing raids on the Spanish ranches that had been carved out of the pasture lands of the former Mission San Juan Bautista.

The *Casa* or house itself was an immense adobe building with walls three feet thick. The windows, all high above the ground, were closed up tightly at night with heavy wooden shutters. The one entrance to the house was a wide doorway, protected by a solid wooden door that could be slammed shut instantly in case of an Indian attack and braced with a heavy oak beam. No amount of Indians crowding around could possibly force this door open.

The second floor of the building was a large single room with port holes on all four sides. These were for the defenders to shoot through when warding off attacking Indians. Only the roof of the house was vulnerable. It was covered with thatch made of bull rushes. But so high were the walls that no Indian could possibly climb up and set the building on fire.

Doña Rosario was on her way back to the house from the bake ovens. In the darkness the coyotes were barking even closer and more furiously than ever. She was just about to step quietly in the doorway when a tornado of arrows, whizzing, screeching, singing, passed in a cloud just over her head. Strange forms, howling fiendishly, were springing up out of nowhere in the darkness Doña Rosario fairly jumped through the doorway, but not before the dozen or so women who had been working at the bake ovens almost ran over her in their determined efforts to get inside the house before the half seen Indian attackers should grab them.

Poor Mary Arroyo, being new to the place, had not bolted for the house the instant the others had started and was now the last one in the stampede. An Indian racing behind her, drew his bow to its full length and shot an arrow straight into her back. The force of the blow threw her flat on her face. Realizing fully now her danger she sprang to her feet. With the arrow still sticking in her back she ran. The arrow waved back and forth in the breeze, each movement digging a little more deeply into her back. She was the last one to enter the house, crowding in just as the door was slammed shut and made fast with the oak beam. Estolano, in the struggle, for the moment was forgotten!

Don Manuel, awakened from his sleep by the noise of the running feet and the shouting of the attacking Indians, rushed instinctively up the broad hall stairs to the fortress above, followed by half a dozen young men of the household: Tony, José María, Gracia, Manuel, Dolores, Francisco. Each seized a loaded gun and began shooting through the port holes.

"There, I got that old buck," declared José María.

"And now you take that!" shouted Francisco, as he and the others continued firing at the milling Indians surrounding the *Casa* on all sides.

As the still defiant Indians fell back from the house, a couple of young voices rang out: "Don't forget, Don Manuel, we're going to roast you alive tonight!" Already several of the Indians were raking coals of fire out of the ovens and fastening them to the tips of their arrows.

"We'll set your roof on fire, Don Manuel!" was their raucous boast.

"Along with your own fat old self, your whole family will burn!" others sang out.

With that the Indians began shooting fire arrows high up into the air, aiming them so that they would fall back onto the thatched roof.

Meanwhile, several Indians were working desperately to move the heavy logs that served as bars to the adobe corral where seventy of Don Manuel's saddle horses were penned up for the night.

"While you, Don Manuel, are roasting," jeered the younger Indians, "we will be riding your horses to the Valley. Tomorrow we will be feasting on them!"

Don Manuel had been in many an Indian battle and was familiar with their boasting. He had fought Indians right out on the open plains. Their taunts meant nothing to him.

"Now, sons, don't get excited," coached the old cavalryman. "Keep picking off any Indians that come up close enough for you to be sure you can get them. But don't waste your ammunition firing just to make a noise." With that Don Manuel went down stairs for a moment to make sure everything was all right down there.

"Oh, Manuel!" screamed Doña Rosario, catching sight of her husband. "Make them let me out the door to get Estolano. He is still outside in his hammock on the porch."

Don Manuel was stunned. His wife's plea had dealt him a knock out blow. He gazed about in bewilderment. Half a dozen women with their backs braced against the door were standing, determined that it should not be opened. He knew that they were correct. To all it was certain that an Indian horde would instantly pour into the house if Doña Rosario's demand was granted.

At the same moment there was a voice from the floor pleading: "Why don't someone help?"

Don Manuel looked down in confusion to see who was calling. It was Mary Arroyo lying face down flat on her stomach, the arrow in her back swaying with every breath she took. She was trying hopelessly to get her hand far enough behind her shoulders to seize hold of the shaft. Several had already attempted to pull the arrow from Mary's back but had been unable to do so, the point was so deeply imbedded in her flesh.

"Oh, no, no, Mary," shouted Don Manuel. "No one can pull an arrow straight out of a wound. The barbs hold it. I'll have to cut it out for you. Here," he commanded, "someone hold a light so that I can see."

Don Manuel knelt down beside the moaning girl. Several held candles close. Tearing the blood soaked dress from Mary's shoulders and holding down her body firmly on the floor with his knee, Don Manuel quickly, resolutely, with a butcher knife dug the arrow out of the screaming girl's back.

"There, now," he ordered as he tossed the bloody arrow head on the table, "you women wash the wound for the girl and poultice it well."

Ignoring Doña Rosario's hopeless plea, Don Manuel raced back up the stairs. Looking out the port-holes the outmaneuvered old warrior was quick to realize that the Indians were winning their battle. Already the gate to the corral was open. He could also smell smoke. His only hope was that the fires in the roof would die out. As for the horses, they were jumping one by one over the lowest log of the gate as the Indians kept forcing them out of the corral. Indians by the dozens were jumping on the backs of the startled horses and heading them towards the eastern mountains and the San Joaquin Valley beyond.

"There goes Regalo, father," shouted one of the boys as an Indian succeeded in mounting Don Manuel's favorite saddle horse.

"And there goes my Colorado," wailed Francisco. At that moment the last of the seventy horses was going out of the corral.

Francisco whistled. He hoped Colorado could hear him. He wondered if in all the excitement his pet horse would remember. Francisco had trained Colorado to come to him whenever he whistled for him. The horse had become so well trained that he would surmount any obstacle in getting to Francisco.

Colorado heard. He promptly bucked the surprised Indian on his back to the ground and, trotting proudly back to the *Casa,* began looking for Francisco.

"Come on out, Francisco," Colorado seemed to be saying by his whinnying. "I'm outside waiting for you."

The few remaining Indians, now left behind by their well-mounted companions, were busy gathering up the dead. All suddenly disappeared as though the earth and the night had swallowed them up.

Colorado was still whinnying outside the house.

"Father," begged Francisco, "let me get on my horse and ride to San Juan Bautista for help."

The face of the old warrior was stern.

"Everything waits until I get to Estolano!"

With that Don Manuel rushed down the stairs. Throwing open the huge door he ran to the hammock. Arrows, shot from all sides, were sticking in it like pins in a pin cushion. Pulling open the hammock Don Manuel gazed within. The little bed was empty!

Bellowing in a towering rage, the old Indian fighter stormed back into the *Casa*.

"Los Indios!

"They've stolen Estolano!"

San Juan Mission 1867

Chapter II

THE INDIAN VILLAGE

ESTOLANO HAD NOT the least fear of Indians. He had been accustomed to them all his life. But he kept wondering why he was being carried so far from home. As it was getting daylight he became more anxious than ever to know what it was all about. But when the burly Indian who had been carrying him in his arms all night finally set him down in broad daylight in the midst of a teeming Indian village then it was that his little eyes really opened wide in amazement.

The stolen horses from the Santa Ana were just beginning to arrive in the village and were being driven into a large brush enclosure. All was hilarity. Indian women and children were running about everywhere in excitement. Everyone was happy. Now there would be an abundance of food for all. For some time there would be no more hunger in the camp.

"See what I stole," shouted Estolano's Indian to an old squaw. "A little white boy!"

Estolano was immediately the center of attention. Swarms of Indian children, none of whom had ever known what it was to wear clothing, began crowding around the little white stranger. His nightgown was a great puzzle to all. Many came timidly forward and felt of the little white covering.

"Little white boy want to be little Indian boy?" inquired the old squaw who had Estolano in charge. She tugged suggestingly at removing his gown.

Estolano, eager to copy after the other children, pulled his nightgown off over his head. He chuckled with glee and stood first on one foot and then another. Never before in his life had he felt so free and unhampered. Like a little bird just ready to flap its wings and soar off in its first flight, he was supremely happy.

"And now some breakfast for the 'mandante'?" asked the old squaw laughing.

Breakfast in this Indian village consisted only of *pinole*. This was made from wild grass seeds pounded very fine in a stone mortar. A little honey was often stirred in for sweetening. This mixture, with a little water added, was heated in a tightly woven basket by having red hot stones dropped in from time to time to keep the mass bubbling. When sufficiently cooked it was allowed to cool and then was ready to eat.

Little Indian hands were soon dipping into the mush the old woman had been preparing for some time and were bringing out heaping handfuls of the sticky mass. Estolano was quick to imitate his Indian companions and was soon gobbling up *pinole* as greedily as the rest of them. After scooping up only a few handsful he could lick his little fingers in true Indian style.

"My, but this is good!" declared Estolano to the old squaw.

"Little white boy much hungry?" she asked. "Plenty much horse meat soon!"

Huge fires were being built in various parts of the rancherie and a cloud of dense black smoke was pouring forth into the sky. A dozen or more horses had been singled out for slaughter. Arrows were shot directly into the heart and first one horse and then another tumbled to the ground.

Soon groups of Indians were working over each dead animal. First the skin was stripped off. Then the lean meat was cut into strips and hung up on long rawhide lines to dry in the sun for "jerky." Hungry Indians were at the same time cutting off big chunks of meat and roasting them on sharp sticks before the roaring fires.

The children of the village were revelling in the blood and gore of the butchering. Estolano, like all the rest, quickly became splattered with blood. Soon it would have been impossible to pick him out from the real Indian children. As he continued to play his body and face became as crimson as though he had painted himself. Estolano was having the greatest excitement of his life. For the first time he was enjoying perfect freedom. The most fun of all was in helping the other children tear the eyes out of the heads of the dead horses and using them to pelt each other with.

Suddenly at midday a large group of horsemen was seen in the distance coming on the dead run. Warning shouts arose at once from all parts of the village and instantly every Indian, large and small, young and old, darted out of sight for safety into the woods like frightened animals. Almost before he knew that anything was happening Estolano found himself all alone in the village. Crouching down behind a newly killed horse, Estolano tried to hide himself from the oncoming danger, whatever it was, that threatened the camp.

Don Manuel, leading the band of horsemen himself, rode directly into the center of the village. In vain he looked for Estolano. Dismounting from his horse he walked boldly into first one deserted Indian tepee and then another, hoping to find Estolano coiled up somewhere peacefully sleeping.

Coming outside the last tepee Don Manuel caught sight of a blood-covered little savage in the distance trying to hide behind one of the dead horses.

"Come on out here," ordered Don Manuel as he strode over to the abandoned child.

The blood smeared face of Estolano peeked out roguishly at him over the dead horse.

"Estolano!" shrieked Don Manuel in horror.

After a brief moment of anxiety Don Manuel realized from Estolano's smile that he was unharmed.

"You little butcher!" shouted Don Manuel, a smile spreading over his face. "Come with me down to the creek."

Estolano realized that his life of freedom was at an end and followed meekly.

"I'll take some of this Indian out of you," declared Don Manuel, his anxiety now turning to disgust. He soused Estolano up and down in the running water. "Now wash the blood off of your face and do it quick."

While Estolano and his father were at the creek several members of the posse noticed an Indian on horseback fleeing up the canyon at breakneck speed. They realized at once that it was on Regalo, Don Manuel's famous horse, that the Indian was riding. Three horsemen immediately set out in pursuit.

When the fleeing Indian saw that he was being followed and would soon be overtaken in the headwaters of the creek he jumped from Regalo's back and ducked head foremost under a manzanita bush. In his excitement the Indians did not realize that although his head and body were hidden his feet were still sticking out in plain sight.

While one horseman rode ahead to lasso Regalo the other two gave their attention to the hiding Indian. Throwing his rope over the Indian's kicking feet the first horseman put spurs to his horse and yanked the astonished Indian clear out into the open in the bright sunlight. While the one *vaquero* held his rope tight on the prisoner the second rider dismounted and tied the wild man's hands securely behind his back. Leading Regalo behind them the three horsemen then drove the helpless Indian before them like a wild steer back to the Indian village.

In the meantime the horses that were still living had been turned out of the enclosure in which they had been held for slaughter and were already on their way back to the Santa Ana.

Don Manuel, with the saddle again on Regalo, was riding home in triumph. Estolano, he held in his arms snugly wrapped up in his serape.

"I didn't have a nice horse like Regalo to ride last night," confided Estolano to his father. "When I woke up the Indian who was carrying me in his arms tried to make me walk. But I couldn't keep up with him. He ran so fast."

The indulgent old Don, now that his son was safe, was delighted to hear Estolano telling of his experiences.

"But why did you come and get me, Papa?" asked Estolano innocently. "I was having such a good time."

Far from being angered Don Manuel was pleased at the self reliance so early manifested in his little son.

"You are a true Catalonian!" declared Don Manuel proudly.

Don Estolano Larios (born 1855) and Señora Altagracia
Higuera de Barcelon y Alvarado (His Half Sister born 1840)
Photo Taken in 1938

Chapter III

THE CHILDREN OF THE SANTA ANA

THE INDIAN children at the Santa Ana and those of Don Manuel's household all played together indiscriminately. The large spring around which the ranch buildings had been built flowed in a steady stream throughout the year, and the escaping waters formed a large pond or lake a short distance from the house. The Indians of the rancho assured Estolano that the running water had a way of talking to people and that if he listened he could tell what it was saying. But although Estolano listened ever so carefully he never was able to make out just what the murmuring waters were trying to tell. They chuckled as they gurgled along on their way to the lake. They seemed to be urging some little boy to wander farther and farther away from home and see what there was beyond the lake and the hill behind it.

But it was only in company with other children that Estolano ventured along the edge of the lake. Sometimes they would find a wild duck's nest and take the eggs home with them. Here they placed them under some unsuspecting hen. In due time the ducklings would hatch out. Then for weeks the faithful old hen scratched worms for them in the daytime and at night protected them from the cold by hovering over them, tent like, with her fluffy feathers. The latter part of the summer the children watched their pets floating majestically on the waters of the lake along with the other wild ducks. Finally in the fall in spite of all that the busy little Estolano and the other children could do in the way of throwing tempting grain on the banks for them the ducks would all fly away never to be seen again, unless perhaps the new arrivals the next spring time were some of the same flock that had flown away the fall before.

The family *carreta* in which Estolano and his mother always rode to San Juan was drawn by two fast-stepping oxen. An Indian driver walked beside the two-wheeled, lumbering vehicle. He had a long, sharp pointed pole with which he punched the oxen from time to time to keep them moving. A bucket of tallow hung from the end of the *carreta* and whenever the wheels began screeching the Indian would pour some tallow on the wooden axles. It took hours to make the journey from the Santa Ana the twelve miles to the Mission. In order to reach San Juan in time for Mass it was necessary often to start long before daylight.

The floor of the *carreta* was carpeted with several huge cow hides. Over this covering were scattered lots of sheep and goat skins together with feather pillows, some nearly as large as feather beds. These were to absorb the jolts of the *carreta* as it rolled over the rough *camino,* or road. To prevent people from falling out of the moving vehicle a wicker basket-like frame three or four feet high surrounded the floor on all four sides.

These were the most contented if not the happiest days of Doña Rosario's life. Though middle-aged, she was still a beautiful woman. She was sure of Don Manuel's love for her. Sitting on the floor of the *carreta* and leaning back comfortably against the wicker work, she realized that she lacked for nothing. She had everything in the world to make her happy. Her older children, now mostly grown, had been taken right into the home of Don Manuel and his children and her children formed one large happy family. Estolano, the half brother of all, was the idol of the household.

On Sundays the Plaza in front of the Mission church was always filled to overflowing with *carretas* from the surrounding ranches. Oxen were tied to every available tree. Although starting hours later from the Santa Ana, Don Manuel and the rest of the family always arrived in ample time for Mass, each one riding his or her favorite saddle horse. Estolano was invariably the first one of the family into the old Mission chapel, even before his mother had time to step down from the high-wheeled *carreta*.

After Mass Estolano and his mother would often go over to the home of Doña Alta Gracia Ursua across the Plaza and visit. They would usually remain over until the next day before returning to Santa Ana. Doña Alta Gracia was a tiny woman, the sister of Father Anzar and the *comadre* of Doña Rosario.

Sometimes, on arriving in San Juan, Estolano would be surprised to find a large corral built on the Plaza. In the afternoon all would sit on the balcony of the Ursua house overlooking the corral and watch a bull and bear play together. At least so Estolano thought. They were so comical, yet so clumsy. The bull would knock the bear over backwards and then poke the animal in the ribs with its horn. This would make the bear so angry that its roar nearly scared Estolano into running away from the Plaza.

In the evening after the candles were lit many of the friends in San Juan of the Ursua family and Doña Rosario would come in to spend the evening. Guitars soon began to hum and the younger people danced while the older ones looked on admiringly. But Estolano knew nothing of all this for the music, instead of coaxing him to dance, sent him at once soundly asleep in his mother's arms.

The return to the Santa Ana began the next morning and occupied most of the day. At the San Benito River, about half way home, the oxen would be given a rest while Estolano and his mother shared their lunch with the Indian driver. *Empanadas,* or meat pies, were the favorite of the hungry little Estolano. Then for a couple of hours a siesta was taken lying on the banks of the river. But it was little sleep that Doña Rosario got, ever-busy as she was trying to tame the restless spirit of her little son.

The last time that Estolano and his mother stayed at the Ursua home, Estolano's mother, as they were leaving, cried and cried. Big American wagons were in the Plaza in front of the Ursua house. Much of the belongings of the Ursua family had been taken out of the house and was packed in the wagons. The Ursua family was going back to their old home in Mexico to live. They were going by way of the Colorado River and would be weeks on the way. Doña Rosario realized that this was the last time she would ever visit with the Ursua family. Even Doña Alta Gracia herself was crying. Estolano was secretly glad when he and his mother were in their *carreta* and on their way back to the Santa Ana. He was greatly puzzled why grown people should cry.

The children at the Santa Ana were so mean. They used to shoot lizards with their bows and arrows. On cold mornings at the beginning of winter these poor lizards would wriggle out of the crevices in the adobe walls of the corral and lie on the flat surfaces sunning themselves. A good shot, and the arrow would tear a soft-bellied lizard all to pieces.

Estolano was busy whittling out an arrow to take the place of the one he had been shooting and had lost. He was sitting close to the outdoor fireplace trying to keep himself warm as he whittled industriously away.

He was toasting himself nicely. His foot was nearly touching the fire. Suddenly he felt his leg getting unusually warm. He looked down to see. His pant leg was on fire! Jumping up he ran as fast as he could, thinking to get away from the heat. But the faster he ran the hotter his leg became and the more his clothes flared up into flame.

The other children chased after him and soon ran him down. Knocking him flat on his face they began throwing dirt over him to put out the fire. By the time the Indians from the house got there the half buried Estolano was screaming at the top of his lungs.

The famous Scotch surgeon of San Juan, Dr. MacDougall, was sent for but by the time he had arrived on horseback Estolano had lost consciousness. After examining the burned leg very critically the doctor began laying out his knives and other instruments.

Don Manuel was looking on in astonishment. "What are you going to do?" he demanded in alarm.

The European doctor looked up in surprise that anyone should question his medical judgment.

"I'm going to cut off this little boy's leg," he replied decisively.

Breaking Horses and Youngsters Together

(This and the following sketches are by Adelaide Maria Barcelon de Martin)

Chapter IV

MADAM PILAR

MADAM Pilar, Don Manuel's sister, was one of the most active women in the little Mission town of San Juan Bautista. Besides tending her four children, Juliana, Refugio, Juan and Ramon, she was the midwife and herb doctor of the whole community.

"Sister Pilar," said Don Manuel, standing in the doorway and holding Estolano in his arms, "I have brought my little son to you to cure. His leg is badly burned. The Scotch Doctor wants to cut it off."

"How ridiculous!" exclaimed his sister as she peered searchingly at the little child in her brother's arms. "Bring him right in, Manuel. With herbs even the impossible is attainable."

The frightened Estolano clung more tightly than ever to his father's neck as his aunt tried to take him in her arms.

"There now, little precious. I won't touch your sore leg." With that she laid Estolano on the bed and softly unwrapped the swathings from the burned limb. "Just let me look at it."

"Merciful heavens!" exclaimed the herb doctor, as she looked up into her brother's face. "Don't you take any care of your children at all? Such a burn is terrible."

"I know it, Pilar. But that's not here nor there now. What I ask you to do is to care for him."

"I'll do my best, Manuel."

Months later it was again Spring in San Juan. Estolano's leg was so far healed that he was able to romp and play with his cousins and once more take an interest in the world about him.

What puzzled Estolano most of all at his aunt's home, he was no longer considered the most important person in the household, as he had always been at his home at the Santa Ana. Here at his Aunt Pilar's, instead of doing just as he pleased, he was made to mind just like all the rest of the children.

Ramon, who was about ten years old, was by far Estolano's favorite among his cousins. Ramon was smart. Ramon could ride a horse. What seemed to Estolano most marvelous of all, Ramon could throw a rope and make it go over a calf's head.

One afternoon Ramon and another boy friend, Charley, were riding on the back of a tame ox around the streets of the little Mission town. They had a bottle of wine between them and were singing at the top of their young voices. Half the children of the village were following behind the merry singers, prodding the weary ox with sticks every once in a while, trying to make him jump and throw the boys off.

"Come here!" shouted Madam Pilar as the two boys came riding proudly past her door.

"Ramon, I tell you. Get down off of that ox right now and come to me."

Reluctantly Ramon slid off the back of the huge ox. Shoving stubbornly first one foot forward and then the other, he finally came inside the house.

Estolano was looking on in wonderment. His aunt had a short leather whip in her hand.

"Take off your coat!"

Ramon did what he knew he had to do.

"Now get down on your knees."

Ramon knelt in front of his mother.

Madam Pilar gave her son a resounding wallop over his

shoulders with this short whip.

Ramon flinched.

His mother gave him another and then a third still harder blow. But Ramon stubbornly refused to cry out.

"Now get up and tell that friend of yours I want to see him. Bring him in the house."

Ramon went out doors and soon returned with his bewildered companion.

"Charley, get your coat off!" ordered the stern-faced herb doctor.

The unsuspecting boy did as he was told.

"Get down on your knees."

Ramon began to snicker as he realized Charley's plight.

'Ramon, you get out of doors or I'll give you yours all over again."

Estolano would have followed Ramon out the door but his aunt sharply ordered: "Estolano, you stay right here." Madam Pilar then administered three lashes in rapid succession on Charley's back. The blows were rained down so swiftly on him that all thoughts of resistance were thrashed out of him even before they had time to develop.

'There now, young man, you go home with that ox of yours and let Ramon alone after this."

Charley, deeply humiliated, struggled desperately to pull his coat on over his sore back as he fairly flew out the door.

"Now, Estolano," said his aunt, smiling grimly, "do you see what happens to naughty boys?"

"But I'm not naughty, am I?" asked Estolano with rising alarm.

"No. But sometime you may want to be. I just want you to know what happens to naughty boys."

"But I'm not going to be a naughty boy," insisted Estolano as he threw his short little arms around his aunt's skirts. He smiled up at her in childish innocence. Love and affection were something that Madam Pilar rarely bestowed on anybody. But this afternoon she did something that she had seldom done before. She bent down and kissed Estolano. Her little nephew felt much reassured. He was certain now that his aunt would never even want to whip such a nice little boy as he was determined to be.

Spring, with its rank growth of weeds and herbs and grasses, had spread a green mantle over San Juan and the surrounding countryside. Estolano's leg was now nearly as good as ever.

"Aunt Pilar."

"Yes, Estolano."

"Sometime I want to help you make medicine."

'That's a good boy."

Madam Pilar looked at the earnest face of her nephew.

"I'll take you with me the next time I go out in the fields gathering herbs. I'll show you which are the good plants, and I'll tell you what they will cure." She glanced up to the rafters over the kitchen where various kinds of dried plants were hanging in bunches ready for use. "I see my supply is getting rather low. You and I will have to get busy and dry a lot more. No one ever knows who will be sick next.

Some days later Madam Pilar and Estolano were getting ready to go out in the fields. 'What surprises me, auntie," said her still limping little nephew, 'is that weeds can cure sores."

'Don't say weeds, Estolano. Call them herbs. If you are going to be my helper you must learn to speak correctly. By the way, Estolano, do you know the names of the various herbs that I use? Look at that bunch near the clock. That is Yerba del Jaraso."

"What do they cure?" asked the inquisitive little boy.

'I make a tea from them and use it when the Indians shoot someone with an arrow. It takes the poison out of the wound."

"And what are those other herbs?"

"Those over by the window? That is Yerba de la Vivora, and

I use them when anyone gets bitten by a rattlesnake."

"I know what those are for right over the fireplace."

"Tell me."

"That's when a person has a sore leg. I noticed that you always take some of them when you doctor my leg."

Madam Pilar was delighted at the keen observation of her little patient. "And do you know the name of them?"

Estolano did not.

"I call them Rabbit's Ear. Don't the leaves look like the ears of a rabbit?"

Late that night there was a timid knocking at the door of Madam Pilar's house. *"Comadre,"* wailed a faint voice outside. *"Abre la puerta."* Estolano raised up in his bed and listened in the darkness.

"Save me, Madam Pilar! They are killing me."

"Who's there?" the herb doctor called fearlessly as she rushed to the door and threw it open. Madam Pilar had been accustomed for years to having people come at all hours of the day and night for her services.

In the darkness Estolano could hear someone coming in the house. Madam Pilar soon had a candle lighted. Holding it in one hand and shielding the flame with the other she came forward to see who her visitor was.

"Maggie!" she screamed. "Is it you?"

In the doorway stood Indian Maggie, her eyes bulging out, her face purple and her neck covered with blood.

"They tried to kill me," cried the Indian girl.

"Who?"

"Those white men. They took me up in the cemetery and hanged me."

"Poor little darling," soothed Madam Pilar as she carefully examined the Indian girl's neck. Something—evidently a rope —had peeled most of the skin off."

"They claimed I had the money."

"Of course you didn't have."

"I haven't got anybody's money. They took me up to the big elm in the cemetery. They put a rope around my neck and yanked me up in the air. The rope was so tight it was choking me. 'Now tell us where that money is!'Then they let me down until my feet touched the ground again. Every time they yanked me up in the air they would all shout: 'Now will you tell us where that money is?' "

"Never mind, precious."

"I couldn't tell them. I didn't know."

Estolano had crawled out of bed and was standing beside his aunt. His eyes were fixed on the bleeding neck of this young Indian servant girl.

"Aunt Pilar, can't we cure her?" asked Estolano impatiently. "I know. It's those rabbit ears that we need."

With Estolano closely following at her heels Madam Pilar began stirring up the fire in the fireplace. Soon she had a kettle of water heating. Estolano could hardly wait until his aunt let him put some herbs in the boiling water.

Madam Pilar carefully bathed Indian Maggie's swollen neck and face. Estolano watched intently. Then she took a nice clean towel and bound a poultice of rabbit's ear around the girl's neck.

"Now Maggie," said the herb doctor assuringly, "get into bed and go to sleep. Soon my little nephew and I will have you cured." Then she added thoughtfully: "You don't need ever to go back to those wicked Americans. You can live here with us." In the darkness Estolano could hear the Indian girl crying herself to sleep.

"Sleep," whispered the herb doctor to her little nephew, "is the best remedy I know of."

Chapter V

MARTINA'S VOW

IT WAS NOW TIME for Martina to pay her vow. Estolano had so far recovered that soon he was to be taken home again. Martina was Don Manuel's favorite daughter. She was short and stout and from her habit of carrying large bundles of clothes on the top of her head walked very erect and fearless. She was so little that when she was being dressed for her wedding she had to stand on a big foot stool. In her white silk wedding dress over her four flouncing underskirts so tiny was her waist that she looked like a fast spinning top.

Melicío, her jovial husband, though still only in his twenties, weighed over two hundred pounds and was six feet tall. He was so powerful that he could give a person merely a slap and knock him down. He could eat the whole side of a lamb at one meal. When eating fish and quail he would chew up bones and all. "The bones are the best part," he always claimed good naturedly. Another big eater was his friend, Mariano. He and Melicio were rivals in good eating. When sitting opposite each other at barbecues they would often grunt at each other in good-natured derision, calling out one to the other: *"Chuco!"* meaning "You hog!"

"But Martina," argued her husband, 'you can't possibly balance that Santa Ana statue on your head. It weighs fully thirty pounds. And remember," Melicio added, "it is twelve miles from here to the Mission."

"I have made my vow," declared Martina spunkily, "and I'll carry it out even if it kills me."

Saint Ann was the patron saint of Don Manuel. Santa Ana, as she is known in Spanish, was the mother of the Virgin Mary. When later in life Don Manuel came into possession of his large grant of land some four leagues east of the Mission he made his patron saint, Santa Ana, the patron saint of his ranch as well. Santa Ana Peak, far to the eastern horizon, towered benignly over his vast holdings.

In honor of Santa Ana he built a chapel on his ranch and every year on her feast day, the 26th of July, he gave a fiesta that usually lasted a week. Relatives and friends from as far away as Monterey were summoned well in advance and Don Manuel kept open house. The fiesta began with Mass said in the ranch chapel. Then followed, in the daytime, horse racing and bull and bear fights, while dancing in the *ramada* or pavilion lasted every night as long as anyone was wide awake enough to stand up and dance.

In the ranch chapel far up in front in the place of honor stood an almost life-sized statue of Santa Ana. It was before this statue that Martina in her hour of agony over the almost fatal burning of her little brother had knelt down and made her vow.

"I have come, father," said Martina reverently as she was asked to step inside the *sala* or reception room of the old Mission of San Juan Bautista, "on an errand of great importance to me."

"You may discuss your errand with greatest confidence," said the young priest.

"I wish to fulfill my vow."

The young priest looked up in astonishment.

"Vow? What vow have you made?"

"I have spoken a vow perhaps too quickly, and perhaps not

too well."

"People often do," agreed the pastor.

"When my little brother, Estolano, was burned almost to death at the ranch, in my anxiety for his recovery, father, I rushed into our ranch chapel and kneeling before the statue of Santa Ana, our patron saint, I made the vow to the holy one that if she would secure the recovery of my little brother I would have a Mass said at your Mission in the saint's honor."

"That was very laudable," said the priest.

"In my anguish, however, father, l confess that I went too far. I promised Santa Ana that I would carry her statue on foot from the ranch chapel to the Mission and have it placed on the High Altar for the services."

"I fear, sister, that you have undertaken more than your strength will allow. A vow, you must remember, is something that should never be made in haste, nor beyond one's means of fulfilling."

"But, father, I must carry out my vow."

"Yes, if you are able."

"I confess, father, that I did wrong," pleaded Martina, "but my only request is that you will say the Mass when I arrive with the statue."

"That I promise," said the priest, firmly. "Will Sunday next meet with your wishes?"

"Yes, father."

At midnight Martina with the four foot statue of Santa Ana firmly fastened with thongs of rawhide to the top of her head, stepped bravely out the door of the Santa Ana ranch house on her way through the darkness the twelve miles to Mission San Juan Bautista. Fortunately she had chosen a time when the full moon was shining and she had little difficulty in making her way along the *camino* or ox cart road. Walking slowly but very erect she was able to keep the tall statue balanced on the top of her head.

Martina had never walked twelve miles before all at one time. She tried to calculate as she made her way slowly forward how long it would take her to reach the Mission. She wondered how tired she would be when she got there.

Martina was glad that her husband was with her. Melicio was riding right behind her on his best saddle horse ready to protect her against the grizzly bears that might be roaming in the darkness and the wild bulls that would most certainly try to attack her when daylight came.

"Melicio?" asked Martina anxiously.

"Yes, darling."

"Can you see me?"

"Yes, dear."

"You won't let your horse get so close he will step on me, will you?"

"No, dear."

"Melicio, have you seen any bears yet?"

All was finally silence. Melicio was somewhat uneasy lest the light of the moon shining on the gold decorations of the statue would be reflected some distance away. He feared it might attract wild animals.

Martina trudged forward bravely hour after hour with no pause or rest. Melicio walked his horse slowly and kept about ten feet behind her. He would gladly have changed places with his wife but he knew her stubborn determination and that his offer would only be scoffed at.

When it came daylight the two were still miles from the Mission. Cattle, here, there and everywhere, could be seen scattered about on the plain. Some were feeding quietly while others more lazy than the rest were awkwardly getting up off the ground, stretching themselves, and then looking around for a good place to begin satisfying their hunger.

As it became broad daylight the bulls, always looking for something to attack, noticed the strange spectacle coming.

They were used to men on horseback and were wary about attacking them. But a person on foot was something strange to them. Such an object looked like some new kind of animal and they were prompt in their readiness to attack.

Martina, in addition to her fatigue, was trembling with fear. Bulls were coming from all directions. They were bawling loudly and pawing dirt over their backs as they came to the attack. Some got so close to Martina that she could feel the hot breath from their snorting nostrils. It was all that Melicio could do at times to drive the angry beasts away. Forcing his horse right up against their sides he would shove them away by main force, at the same time slashing them in the eyes and face with his lariat and quirt to give them something else to think about besides attacking Martina.

The crossing of the San Benito River began to worry Martina. She knew that the stream was usually about knee deep in the spring of the year. She wondered whether she might collapse in the water and the weight of the statue strapped to her head hold her face under water until she drowned. But when she came to the stream she resolutely pulled up her long skirts to her knees and stepped into the cold, swiftly flowing water. Her prayer was continually for strength to enable her to keep going until she reached the Mission.

Leaving the river she plunged straight across country towards the white adobe church on the hillside in the distance. The Mission bells were ringing. She could hear them now. They seemed to be saying to her: "Keep coming, Martina. Keep coming, Martina!"

As she entered the Mission orchard she could see the plaza above filled to overflowing with people. Cheer after cheer was being given to encourage her. She made her way slowly up the hillside. The young priest was waiting at the church door to receive the statue. It was carefully removed from the top of her head. She was almost giddy for the moment, her head felt so light. With the lifting of the burden from her head the fatigue for the moment was gone.

A procession was formed. With the young priest leading, followed by Martina, it made its way up the center of the long Mission church. The heavy statue was placed on the high altar, Martina knelt on the hard, brick floor in a prayer of thanksgiving and the services commenced. At the reading of the Gospel the young priest preached a sermon. He praised Martina for her devotion in carrying out her vow. "Not one of you people within the sound of my voice," said the priest as he looked out over the vast congregation that filled the Mission church to overflowing, "would have made the vow that Martina made in the hopes of saving her little brother. And I go farther in saying," declared the young priest, "that if any of you had ever made such a vow you would not have had—may I speak vulgarly—the guts to fulfill it."

When the services were over and Martina attempted to rise —she couldn't. Her strength had ebbed away entirely. She was carried on a cowhide litter to the Ranchito, the new home of Don Manuel just at the edge of San Juan.

When Don Manuel had heard what his daughter was doing that Sunday morning he was furious. Days later when Martina was strong enough for him to talk with her he sternly upbraided her. "Don't you ever make a vow like that again. If any of my children get hurt in the future, you let them get well with what help we are able to give them. But no more of these vows!"

Martina needed no words from her father. She was cured of her rashness. "I have had punishment enough," admitted the wan-faced Martina as she looked up, again childlike, into her father's face.

Chapter VI

THE RANCHITO

IT WAS INTO an entirely new world that Estolano was ushered when he was brought home after his winter spent with his Aunt Pilar. During his absence the family had moved from the Santa Ana ranch and were now permanently located at the Ranchito, Don Manuel's little ranch of four thousand acres adjoining the Mission town of San Juan Bautista.

The house at the Ranchito was a large two-story adobe building roofed with tile. It consisted of some forty rooms. Verandas were a very conspicuous feature of the house. There were two in front. One was upstairs and the other down. They were set deeply inside the house. The front of the verandas was even with the outside walls of the building. On each side of the main entrance into the house were two very fancy benches ten feet or more long where visitors in the hot afternoon could sit in the shade and rest. In front of the house was the Patio. This was simply a large front yard. It was surrounded with a wooden fence with gates on each side near the house and a front gate that opened out into the orchard and vineyard. Along the fence were hollyhocks and rose bushes.

On the south side of the house was the *"Plaza"* where the bull fights were held. Along the second story of the house, facing the bull ring, was a long open veranda where the women and children could sit in safety and look down on the bull fights.

Along the west and north sides of the house was a low one-story addition containing the kitchen, the dining room, store rooms and quarters for the Indian servants.

The glory of the house was its *"sala"* or main living room. It was some fifty by seventy feet in size and was the indoor scene of all the family festivities. It was the dance hall, the children's play room and the main dining room, all in one. Across the room and opposite the main entrance from the veranda was the fireplace. It was large enough to take three-foot wood and was quite modern, being built of brick. The large stairway leading to the second floor was at the left end of the room. There were any number of small rooms or bedrooms, opening off from the sides of the main hall. The family dining room was on the north side of the house and was reached through a hallway leading from the main room. The kitchen, almost as large, adjoined the dining room.

Don Manuel's room was on the south side of the building and was entered from the *Sala* through a doorway at the foot of the stairs. Adjoining this room was the trunk room where each member of the family had a trunk of his own in which were kept his clothes and personal belongings.

On the second floor there was a room called *El Cuerto de Las Armas*. It was the Armory room and was on the southwest corner adjoining the balcony overlooking the bull ring. Don Manuel had been a Lieutenant of Militia under the Mexican government for years. In this room were stored dozens of flint lock guns, saddle pistols, machettes, sabres, a lance or two and a shield for warding off Indian arrows. This shield had seen lots of service but was now quite a curiosity. It was about two feet in diameter and was perfectly round. It was made out of pressed rawhide more than an inch thick and was as hard as iron. On the inside of the shield, which was curved, there was a place to slip one's arm through and a hand-hold.

On the upper floor was another large hall corresponding to the main hall on the floor below. Around this upper hall were room after room, all opening into the hall. Double doors from the upper front veranda opened into this hall. Along the whole south side of the second floor was the wide enclosed veranda overlooking the bull ring.

Only the inside windows and those in Don Manuel's room had glass. The rest had iron bars and wooden shutters. The iron bars were on the outside of the windows and the wooden shutters were fitted into place from the inside. At night the shutters were put up and in the morning taken down. It was dark, of course, when the shutters were closed. But that didn't matter. As it was night, candles had to be kept lit anyway.

The sugar room was kept under lock and key. It was on the second floor on the front of the house and right next to the arena balcony. Sugar was bought in barrels. It was cube sugar. The reason for the sugar room was to keep the sugar out of reach of the dozen or more children that lived at the Ranchito.

The main hall served mostly for parties and dancing. Large family dinners were also served there. The family table was perhaps twenty feet long. At least four people could sit at the ends. Around the wall of the room were long wooden benches. All along the walls were holders for placing candles to light the room.

At the door to Don Manuel's room stood the grandfather's clock that Estolano's father prized so highly and for which he had bartered hundreds of hides on a trading ship years before in Monterey Bay. Right beside the clock was the *"tinaja"* or Mexican water jar. It held half a barrel of water. It sat on the floor and was three or four feet high. It was kept filled with drinking water which was always almost ice cold. It was one of the famous water jars from Guadalajara, Mexico. Along side of the water jar there was a little table. On this was a decanter of wine. Also sugar, glasses and a dipper. The children of the

Ranchito would imitate their elders by taking a dipper of water, add some sugar and pour in a little wine. They were always thirsty or thought they were.

Beside the hallway leading into the family dining room, there was a cupboard filled with goblets, each hanging by its tail. There was a decanter of brandy in the cupboard and also some wine. As each cowboy filed past on his way into the dining room he would stop and pour himself out his choice of drinks. The wine was always slighted, but not so the grape brandy.

Don Manuel's room was the only one with furniture from abroad. All the other furniture in the Ranchito was of home manufacture. Don Manuel's bedstead was of rosewood. Nearby were two tables, one round and the other square. There was also a sofa covered with black mohair or horsehair. On a shelf in the corner of the room was a clock about two feet high. It was behind this unassuming clock that Estolano's father used to keep his money hidden.

Although there were many fireplaces in the Ranchito adobe, yet none were ever used for cooking. They were used simply for heating the house in the winter when the weather was cold. Live oak wood was always used. It was wonderful wood. There would always be fire in the ashes in the morning. All that would be necessary was to put some shavings on the coals in order to start the fire blazing again.

Besides the fireplace in the kitchen, there was also a large iron cook stove. It had six or eight lids and an oven large enough to roast a little pig in whole. Small iron spits were used to roast meat in front of the iron stove. The front doors would be opened, the coals raked down and the meat held on the spit and roasted. Outdoors there was a large brick oven where the bread was baked. There were also several *hornillas* outside the house. These were holes in the ground lined with rocks. On the top was the *comal,* a flat piece of iron. Underneath a fire was built and on the top of the *comal* tortillas were baked.

Feather beds and feather pillows were unknown in Estolano's early home. Bedsteads were made out of lumber and were home made. Instead of slats and springs there was practically a solid floor of boards. On this was placed a tick filled with straw or corn husks. On top of this was a mattress stuffed with wool.

Once each year the mattresses were all taken up stairs into the big hall and the wool dumped out on the floor. Then Estolano and the other children of the Ranchito would be put to work with willow switches beating the wool until it was all fluffy again. The mattresses were restuffed, being tied every little ways as the stuffing progressed. When the tick was full the side would be fastened again and the mattress was ready for another year. Pillows were also made by stuffing them with wool.

There were five meals a day at the Ranchito. The first breakfast, called in Spanish *"desayuno,"* was at any time of the morning that a person happened to get up. Each would find his own way down to the kitchen where he was served his choice of either chocolate, coffee or gruel, together with bread and butter. The family never gathered together at the table all at one time for this meal.

Don Manuel himself was always served in bed. He drank *Mate,* a tea imported from South America. He had a solid silver cup shaped like an urn, and with a handle on either end. A round lid fitted snuggly over the top. A platinum tube ran through the lid. On the end at the bottom was a perforated bulb. Through this tube Don Manuel sucked the liquid up into his mouth. Estolano often helped his father sip this tea and thought it most delicious.

The real breakfast at the Ranchito was at ten o'clock. This meal was called in Spanish *almuerzo.* Beans, fried eggs and bread were served. Tortillas made out of either wheat flour or corn meal were always eaten. These served hot with butter were fine. Chocolate made with milk was the drink. Fresh eggs, the whites separated from the yolks, were beaten up and a little of each dropped into the cups of chocolate. A dash of grated nutmeg on top was added.

Lunch was a light meal served at one o'clock. It was called *merienda.* Pumpkin preserves, cheese and tea constituted the meal.

Tea, or *colacion,* was at four o'clock. *Tostados* or rolls were served at this meal. They were split open and spread with butter. Cheese and nuts were also eaten. Tea, of course, was the beverage. This was a wild tea made from *yerba buena,* a kind of mint that grew wild right there on the Ranchito.

Cena, or supper, was the big meal of the day and was served at eight o'clock in the evening. Beef, beans, potatoes, together with tortillas or bread, was the menu. The beef was either roasted, stewed or broiled. Tea and wine were the beverages. There were no cakes or pies, except on feast days or when someone had a birthday.

Chapter VII

A HUNTER'S PARADISE

DON MANUEL'S RANCHITO or Little Ranch was a tract of four thousand acres (one square league) of land lying on the eastern slope of the Coast mountains. The upper boundary was the crest of the hills where the mountains look down on San Juan. This ridge was known as *La Cuesta de los Pinacates,* meaning Stink Bug Ridge. The right hand side of the ranch adjoined the *Rancho de Las Aromas,* belonging to Don Juan Miguel Anzar. The left boundary was the *Camino Real de en Medio,* the "Middle Road" running over the mountains from San Juan to Monterey. At the foot of the mountains lay the town of San Juan and the lands of the Mission. These were the lower boundaries of the Ranchito.

Long stretches of grassy hillsides made up most of the Ranchito. These were criss-crossed and slashed with ravines and gulches filled with trees and shrubs. Wild gooseberries and blackberries were to be found wherever there was sufficient moisture. *Manpunceres,* a kind of little plum but very sweet, grew in clumps in many places in the hills. Acorns that were almost as good to eat as nuts were borne in large quantities wherever there were oak trees.

The Ranchito was a hunter's paradise. Quails by the thousands lived in the thickets. Robins and other birds were plentiful. The hills were full of deer. Black bears occasionally poked their noses out of the brush and looked sullenly at the human intruders on their domain.

Every little spot on Don Manuel's ranch had its own particular name. *La Cuesta de los Pinacates,* meaning the ridge of the stink bugs, was the name of the crest of hills on the upper part of the ranch. These little stink bugs were particularly thick up there. The laurel patch where Don Manuel and his vaqueros cut their lance poles before going into the battle with the Americans at the Natividad was called the *Palos de Lansa.* At the back of the ranch house ran a little mountain stream. Although it was knee deep in the center and was at least twenty feet wide at times it was called the *Arroyito,* meaning the *Little Creek. Las Piedras* were the huge, wind-carved, echo rocks that answered back whenever a person walked among them and yelled loudly. *Las Iririsis* was the place where the dogwood grew. *Los Berracos* were the buckeyes. *Los Tollones* was the choke cherry patch. *La Cienaga* was the swampy piece of ground quite a ways from the house where the Indian, Miguel, lived and took care of Don Manuel's band of wild hogs.

There was a nice level field along the foot-hills north of the house and it was here that the wheat, barley, corn and beans were raised. Oxen were used for planting and harvesting. At night the ranch laborers would let Estolano and the other children of the Ranchito ride the oxen home. The oxen all had names. A white ox was called *Cisne,* meaning swan. *Coral,* meaning snake, was the name of a black and white fellow. A very gentle old reddish colored ox was called *Granizo* because it had lots of white spots on its back. *Granizo* means hail. Other oxen were named *Tildio,* killdeer, and *Garrion,* linnet. A red ox went by the name *Chilicote,* meaning vine. Hauling wood from the mountains and the field work was all done by oxen. Horses were used only for riding and for the carriage.

The ground in the patio in front of the house was almost as hard as a pavement, and it was here that the threshing was usually done. When the wheat was ripe, it was cut with scythes by hand and then raked up with hand rakes. When it was sufficiently dry, it was hauled in from the field in an ox wagon and stacked in the Patio. The stack was made perfectly round. A circular fence would be rigged up around the stack. Threshing was usually done in the afternoons. Six or eight horses were turned in loose around the stack. A couple of young lads on horseback rode into the enclosure. A man with a pitchfork stood on top of the stack and pitched the grain down onto the ground. The boys drove the band of loose horses around and around the stack until no wheat stem was left whole. The boys all liked to help with the threshing, for they liked to ride. It was fun lashing at the horses ahead and making them run knee deep through the straw.

When all the grain had been tramped, it was necessary to wait for a windy day to winnow it. Three or four Indian women would be brought in to the Patio. They had trays made out of wood and sometimes out of tules. They were shaped like a basket and were called *bateas*. The women would throw up a tray full of the mixture in the air. The wind would blow the chaff away and the grain would fall down in a pile on the ground. Often the grain had to be winnowed two or three times if the wind was not blowing strong enough. In this way the wheat was winnowed very clean.

As soon as one stack of grain was threshed, more grain would be hauled up from the field and stacked again on the threshing floor, ready to be threshed as before. Beans were threshed in the same way as wheat.

There was a grist mill eight or ten miles from San Juan, and it was here that wheat from the Ranchito was taken to be ground. The mill was at the Jesús Hipolito adobe that stood near the *Portezuela* or Gateway on the road from San Juan into the Pajaro Valley. It was on what was then the Vallejo Grant and was about four or five miles south of Watsonville.

The mill was run by ox power.

The Hipolito adobe was a large, two-story house. On the south side was an outside stairway leading to the second story. On the ground floor in the north part of the building there was a large open room. It was here that the mill was located. The mill consisted of two large flat stones, one on top of the other. They were up off the ground about three feet. In the upper stone there was a hole in the center into which a large beam was fitted. This reached to the top of the ceiling and held the upper stone in place. A strong pole or sweep was fastened to the upper stone and an ox hitched to it. In front of the animal was another lighter pole also fastened to the mill stone. The ox was tied to this with a rope. When the ox started going, the stick in front of him would keep leading him on. He would walk round and round for hours and the rocks ground and ground.

At the Ranchito as soon as the wheat and beans were winnowed they were taken upstairs in the house where they were stored in large hogsheads. Whenever flour was needed some of this wheat would be sacked up and taken to Hipolito's mill where it was ground into flour and then brought back to the Ranchito. Along with the flour came the bran and the middlings which were again stored in the hogsheads upstairs until needed.

The vineyard on the Ranchito was right next to the Patio on the north side along the creek. It was planted with Mission grapes. These are small and black but quite sweet. Just below the vineyard was a little patch of ground where quite a lot of peanuts were raised. Farther out front towards the road was the orchard. It consisted of apples, pears and plums. There were no berries except strawberries. Farther out in front, along by the creek was a big garden. It was on the south side of the creek. Water from the creek was used for irrigation. This was not done by furrows or by flooding but by hand sprinklers. Lettuce, onions, garlic and cabbage grew here.

At the Ranchito gate just off of the main road there was a big patch of watermelons, muskmelons and pumpkins. These were raised without irrigation. Over across the creek on the north side was the field where corn and beans were grown. It was here when there were no crops growing that colts were taken to be broken to ride. The ground was fine, nice and soft dirt. It was just the place to land, if a person was bucked off.

The Santa Ana Rancho Buildings

Chapter VIII

THE CHILDREN OF THE RANCHITO

USUALLY NO LESS than three or four extra families lived and kept house at the Ranchito. It was the home place for all the Larios and Higuera families. Whenever any of the sons or daughters would get into difficulties, home to the Ranchito they would come with their families. Each family had its own set of rooms, usually on the second floor. There was Lupe de Salas with her husband and two children. Also living on the same floor was Juana Higuera de Belardez and her husband and five children. For a time Martina Larios de Soto and her family occupied rooms on this floor. Antonio Larios and his wife and two children lived downstairs near the kitchen.

Estolano's sister, Guadalupe, had been sent by Don Manuel when a young girl to Notre Dame, the Sisters School in San Jose. There she learned to play the serafina, to embroider beautifully and to read aloud charmingly. Guadalupe married Luciano Salas, from Sonora, Mexico, and they had two children. For a long time the family lived upstairs in the Ranchito. In the evenings in the winter time a brazier of hot coals would be brought into Don Manuel's room. Don Manuel himself would lie in bed. Others of the family would sit around on the couch and eat raisins and nuts. Guadalupe would put her babies to bed and then come downstairs and read aloud to the family.

Don Manuel's library consisted of a hundred or more volumes. They were kept in a bookcase hollowed out of the adobe wall in Don Manuel's room. Some of the titles were:

Las Mille Uno Noches, with its stories of Sinbad, El Marino, and Aladdin, ó La Lampera Maravillosa.

Don Quijote de la Mancha.

Gil Blas de Santillana.

Los Tres Mosqueteros.

Pablo y Virginia.

El Ultimo Abencerraja. (A story of the Moors in Spain.)

El Collar de la Reina. (The Queen's Necklace.)

Bernardo del Carpio. (This was the story of a famous Spanish swordsman and hero.)

Alonzo Cano. (A funny book that was a great favorite with the boys of the household.)

Los doze Peres de Francia. (All about French knights. Stories of jousts and tournaments.)

Voz de la Naturaloza. (The Voice of Nature. A book of stories for children.)

From their earliest infancy the children of the Ranchito were taught obedience and respect for their elders. The rod was never spared. Stealing, lying, swearing and disrespect were always punished with several hard lashes across the back, usually with a rawhide quirt.

At the age of two or thereabouts, most of the children were able to bless themselves. This is done by making the cross on the forehead, then on the lips, the breast and the body. The words used are:

On the forehead, *"Por la señal de la Santa Cruz"* (By the sign of the Holy Cross). On the lips: *"De nuestros enemigos* (From our enemies), on the breast: *"Libranos, Señor Dios Nuestro"* (Deliver us, O Lord, Our God). Then over the body: *"En el nombre del Padre, del Hijo y del Espiritu Santo. Amen."* (In the name of the Father and of the Son and of the Holy Ghost. Amen.)

When the children were old enough to memorize, they were

taught a few short prayers to recite on their knees at their bedside on retiring and arising. One of these prayers was: "Thanks and praises I give Thee, Great Lord, for having allowed me to see the eventide. In Thy grace and service I pray that Thou wilt let me see the dawn that I may know and believe that there is a God in Heaven, on earth and everywhere, for ever and ever. Amen."

At the age of seven years confessions began.

Don Manuel's grove of laurel on the Ranchito was the only one of its kind in the San Juan neighborhood. On Palm Sunday branches of these laurel were taken to the Mission in San Juan and used in the services in place of palm leaves. After being blessed, they were distributed among the congregation. People would take them home and keep them in their houses. As the families at the Ranchito were so numerous, there was blessed laurel in almost every room of the house.

On stormy nights when there would be rain and heavy winds, accompanied by thunder and lightning, and the people of the Ranchito were frightened, Estolano's mother would go from room to room gathering up these branches of blessed laurel. With a lighted wax candle in her hand and these pieces of laurel she would walk out on the veranda into the storm. She would light the branches, one at a time, and hold them out towards the storm until they were burned out. This was done as an offering to appease the wrath and fury of the storm. With the lighting of each branch she murmured a prayer.

Every morning at the break of day Estolano's mother would sit up in bed and say: *"Ave María Purísima,"* which means "Hail, Holy Queen." The response would be *"Sin pecado original concebida."* Then would follow the singing of this hymn:

> *"Ya viene el alba,*
> *Rompiendo el dia—*
> *Digamos todos*
>   *Ave María!"*

The children of the many families at the Ranchito all played together like one household. All were uncles, aunts, nieces, nephews and cousins of one another. The place was simply running over with little ones.

Estolano, as uncle, was usually the leader in all mischief. His nephews were only too willing to follow his lead. Sugar was something that the children were hungry for at all times. The sugar room at the Ranchito was on the second floor and had a barred window. The door was kept locked. Estolano early discovered that the bars on the outside were wide enough apart for him to crawl through and get into the room. He would go out on the veranda overlooking the bull ring. Then by climbing along the railing he could reach the window sill of the barred window. There was little difficulty for him to stick his head through the bars and then wriggle his body through. Once inside, a whole barrel of sugar cubes was at his disposal. He would fill an old hat, tie a rope to it and let the sugar down to the ground where his nephews were waiting. All would fill their pockets. Estolano, climbing back along the wall, would make his way down stairs. Then he and his helpers would leisurely stroll up the creek together, their hands filled innocently with cold tortillas from the kitchen. On arriving at their camp ground they would fill a wide mouthed bottle with sugar, add water to it and shake well. This made a thick syrup. Then pouring this over the tortillas they would feast royally in their outlaw retreat.

In a little willow grove close to the barbecue grounds there was a stand of eight or ten bee-hives. In the front of each hive there was a small glass window through which a person could see what was going on inside the hive. Estolano and his gang would spy around until they found the hive that showed the most honey. Then they would throw a long rope over the box. Walking to the end of the rope they would yank the hive off of the stand. To escape the fury of the bees the boys would have to run like the mill tail. The bee-hive would come tumbling down the side of the hill. It seldom reached the creek bed for the wooden box would have been demolished before it got half way down. The bees would take fright from the destruction of their home and would collect up in the willow trees. The boys, playing they were wild bears, would go down to the broken hive and gobble up the chunks of honey.

There were many chickens, turkeys and geese at the Ranchito. Their quarters were up along the creek fully two hundred yards west of the house. The ganders were very savage. Mounted on their stick horses and with small ropes for *riatas* the boys would lasso an old gander by the neck and drag it around as long as there was any fight in it. Nearby was a dry creek bed with small willow trees on either side. There the boys would scrape out a shallow hole in the sand and bury the dead goose. The family began noticing that the white ganders were disappearing, but could not guess the cause. When all the ganders, four or five of them, had been dragged to death and buried the boys tackled a turkey gobbler. This proved their undoing. They had to get two or three ropes over the gobbler's neck before they could choke him down and handle him. There was so much hollering going on and so much gobbling on the part of the turkey that the attention of the grown-ups was attracted. The boys were caught as they were dragging the dead turkey to the burying ground. Estolano and his cowboys were forced to confess, and his outlaw band was broken up.

For real fun there was nothing like riding calves. The older boys would saddle up their ponies and go out to rope a young calf. Oftentimes it was a yearling and quite large. They would throw it down and then put a rope around its body for a *surcingle*. When the calf was allowed to get up the boys would hold it with a long rope until one or two of the youngsters could get on its back. Then the calf would be turned loose. The riders held on tight to the *surcingle* as long as they could. As soon as they were thrown off they would get right up and go at it again. Calf riding was genuine fun. It also helped Estolano and the older boys to learn how later on to ride bucking horses.

Estolano and the smaller boys would often play they were holding a bull fight. One boy with a pair of horns tied on his head would be the bull and would try to gore the bull fighters and those who were taking the part of horses and their riders.

Catching bees in hollyhocks was a milder form of amusement. "Biz!" would go the bee when the top end of the flower was pinched shut and the insect found himself a prisoner.

The little girls of the Ranchito had their rag dolls for pets and companions. The height of their mischief was to steal a few cookies and then go out under the trees with their dolls and have a dinner party.

Catotoas, or jacks, was a game played by both boys and girls. For jacks they used marbles. Chilocate plants grew plentifully on the Ranchito. Each pod had four seeds. These large seeds were often used for jacks instead of marbles. The game was to toss one marble up in the air and pick up first one marble, then two at a time and finally all six. If a person failed the turn went to the next player.

In the evenings after supper all the children of the many households were allowed to romp and play in the *Sala* to their hearts' content. There were forfeit games and dancing. But when it came bedtime some mother would call out: *Ave María Purísima."* That was the signal for all to kneel. All joined in the simple prayers. These were generally: First the Apostles' Creed, then "Hail, Holy Queen," followed by "Our Father" and "Confiteor Deo." Then to bed all the children had to go. Obedience was absolute among the children of the Ranchito.

Chapter IX

DON MANUEL'S INDIANS

DON MANUEL'S band of Indians were as much a part of his ranch establishment as were the members of his own family; and, when he moved permanently from the Santa Ana to the Ranchito, he brought them all with him. He had little shacks built for the several families on various parts of the ranch while the single Indians he housed for the most part right in the ranch house itself.

The oldest Indian couple were Desiderio and his wife, Lucata. They were too old to work any more. Their cabin was about half a mile up the creek from the house. Here there was a nice piece of ground, and this old couple busied themselves raising what little corn and beans they needed for their own use. Don Manuel always saw to it that they were furnished with all the beef and mutton they wanted and were well cared for.

Desiderio's wife, Lucata, spoke but very little Spanish. Her greetings always were: *"Amica Luyka,"* which was meant for "Hello, my friend." Her name, Lucata, was Indian.

One time a gopher was throwing up dirt near Desiderio's shack. Only the gopher's head could be seen. Without bothering to get up from the bench where he was sitting Desiderio reached leisurely for a bow and arrow and with them shot the gopher through the neck. The gopher endeavored to get back down its hole, but the arrow through its neck prevented it from doing so. Estolano, who had been watching Desiderio, seized hold of the arrow and brought the gopher still squirming on the stick to the old Indian. Without skinning or cleaning it the Indian threw it on the fire and began roasting it.

"You like eat gopher?" asked Desiderio.

"No! No!" shrieked Estolano, horrified at the thought of eating a gopher, insides and all.

"Him mucho good," urged Desiderio as he lifted the gopher from the fire and bit out a chunk of the thoroughly cooked little animal.

Desiderio was an expert at making bows and arrows and kept the children of the Ranchito well supplied with these weapons. The boys became so expert with these that they could shoot linnets and other little birds as skillfully as the Indians themselves.

A young Indian, Julio, and his wife had their cabin across the creek from the Ranchito house. Both helped with the work in the house when needed. Julio was a kite maker and kept the whole bunch of Ranchito children busy flying kites. He knew how to build kites that would fight each other. He would fix a knife on the tail of a kite. Then by skillful manipulation a boy could maneuver the kite up close to the other kites flying high in the air and cut the strings holding them. The boys would often have kite battles. It was fun to see the loser have to chase his kite for a long distance to recover it. Sometimes cut kites would sail from the Ranchito clear down into the streets of San Juan and even into the Mission orchard.

Felipa was a Tulare Indian girl who had been captured by Don Manuel in the San Joaquin Valley on one of his expeditions in pursuit of Indian marauders. Although very young when captured, she already had four little stripes tatooed down her chin. These stripes were about as wide apart as a lead pencil. She had been raised in Don Manuel's family. When she grew up she married a Yaqui Indian from Mexico named Rosario Garcia. They had no children. They lived in a little house a few hundred yards from Desiderio and Lucata. Rosario had charge of the sheep on the ranch. Felipa was at the Ranchito most every day helping with the housework.

On the upper part of the ranch, about two or three miles from the house, there was a little cabin where Miguel and his wife, Juliana, lived. It was up near the *Cuesta de los Pinacates* (Stink Bug Ridge). They had one son about ten years old. Miguel also was a Yaqui Indian and had come up from Mexico. He took care of the hogs on the Ranchito. There were about three or four hundred of these, mostly razor backs. Miguel's cabin was up near the *cienaga* or swamp. Here the hogs liked to wallow on hot days. In the mornings Miguel, with a long pole over his shoulder and followed by all the hogs, would roam picturesquely over the hills. Miguel would knock the acorns off of the trees for the hogs to feed upon. They throve wonderfully under his care and grew very fat.

Lothario was an old, old Indian, maybe a hundred years of age. He was the only Indian on the Ranchito who refused to wear clothes. He had been in many Indian battles and was all scarred up from the arrows that had struck him. He lived in a little hut all by himself out by the horse corral. Someone in the house always took him his meals. He was so crippled with rheumatism that he was unable to walk. His only mode of locomotion was to push himself along on his haunches. He was continually singing Indian songs. These sounded to Estolano and the other children of the Ranchito simply like grunts. He would pound his knees with his fists as hard as he could to drive out the pain. When his sufferings became too severe, he would change his singing to curses.

Lothario wore only a breech clout for clothing. One time a neighboring boy, named Santana Butron, was visiting at the Ranchito.

"Aren't you cold?" he asked the naked Lothario.

"Is your face cold?" countered Lothario innocently.

"No," replied Santana.

The Indian smiled. "Me all face!"

Lothario had been a hero at the Santa Ana. It was he who had hid Manuelito Larios and Antonio Higuera during one of the many Indian raids there. When the wild Indians from the San Joaquin Valley came into Lothario's house to talk with him, Lothario kept their attention so wrapped up in what he was saying that the Indians went away without ever noticing the two little boys Lothario had carefully hidden in the back of the room behind a side of beef.

Lothario often talked of his younger days and of how he used to hunt deer. His method was to throw the hide of a deer with the horns still on over his shoulders. Then he would jump around and make a noise to attract a deer. Pretty soon a big buck would come out of the brush to see. Lothario would shoot an arrow and wound it. Then coming up closer he would dispatch it with his spear. Lothario claimed that he had killed many a deer this Indian way.

There were four single Indians who worked around the house and the ranch. Their names were Rogaciano, Gaspar, Macedonio and Chicalca. They had their quarters in the shed-like part, built on to the main ranch house. Chicalca was a special favorite. He was Don Manuel's body guard. On one occasion when the wild Indians from the San Joaquin Valley were making a raid on the Santa Ana Ranch. Chicalca saved Don Manuel's life. Larios was in bed at the time the attack began. He heard the commotion but did not know that an Indian attack was in progress. He rushed out a side door to see what was the matter. At the same instant Chicalca came rushing into the house to escape the shower of arrows. The two met head on. Chicalca, by pushing Don Manuel forcibly back into the house, saved Don Manuel's life. Chicalca bolted the door and for hours the Indian raid continued.

On account of this act of fidelity Don Manuel always treated Chicalca extra fine. He dressed Chicalca even better than himself. He often took him visiting places with him. They once went to San Francisco together. On this particular occasion he had Chicalca dressed up like a lawyer or professional man with a long tailed coat, a stove pipe hat, high-heeled boots, white shirt and cravat, cane and gloves. Unmindful of the elegance of his plug hat, Chicalca persisted in wearing his long black Indian hair tied up in a knot at the back of his head. The children of the Ranchito nearly died with laughter when Chicalca, as dignified as a judge, set out with Don Manuel for the city.

After one of the many raids on the Santa Ana Ranch the band of Californians, in pursuing the San Joaquin Indians, came upon an Indian village where the only persons left were a very old woman and a little girl. Don Manuel felt sorry for the little child. He reached down from his horse and lifted her up into the saddle in front of him. The only clothing she had on was a little rabbit skin thrown over her shoulders. Don Manuel wrapped his serape around her and brought her home. They had her christened Gertrudes and raised her right along with the other children of the family. She was only about seven years old when they got her, for she was just beginning to lose her little front teeth. Two of her teeth were gone. She was about the same age as Estolano's older sister, Martina. It was Gertrudes who did most of the grinding with the metate while she lived at Santa Ana.

When Gertrudes grew up a Sonoran from Mexico married her. He was a fine looking Mexican. He was tall, light complexioned and had blue eyes. He was a very fine man. When they were married Don Manuel made Gertrudes a dowery of a house behind the public schoolhouse and four acres of land. He also gave the newlyweds a couple of cows and two saddle horses.

Two other little Indian girls who had been raised in the Larios family lived in the Ranchito house and helped with the housework.

About a quarter of a mile up the creek from the two-story adobe mansion of Don Manuel was the Indian *temescal* or sweat house. It was the community center for the Indians. It stood beside the creek where a dam had been placed to form a pool. The *temescal* was a round, mud-covered house. The Indians when sick would build a hot fire inside and then sit around on the floor with the door tightly closed. When the perspiration was fairly running off of the sick Indian, he would suddenly bolt out of the house and dive headlong into the cold water of the creek. This was Indian medicine.

Although Estolano always liked the Indians, he didn't think much of their medicine and was glad that he didn't have to take any. Even the thought of a plunge in the cold water sent a twinge up his spine. For medicine he much preferred his Aunt Pilar's leaves and salves.

Chapter X

VACCINATION

GOING VISITING was the principal amusement of the older people in the early days at Mission San Juan Bautista. Estolano's mother, Doña Rosario, was a very friendly soul and dearly loved going to her neighbors' houses. She knew everyone in San Juan. Sunday was her great visiting day. It was one of the familiar sights of the little Mission town on these occasions to see Doña Rosario leading Estolano by the hand as the two trudged along the dusty roads that served as streets in San Juan.

The Boronda home was a long adobe house of three rooms. The ceiling was of cloth, and the visitor could see in places the rafters still fastened by rawhide just as Canuto had tied them years before. In the *sala* there was a fireplace large enough to take a whole log at one time. The house stood on *Calle Quarto,* now known as Fourth Street.

Canuto Boronda was a fine looking man. He had been a Spanish soldier in California "in the time of the King." The Boronda house was always full of people. Estolano and his mother often visited there. But Estolano never saw Canuto up and walking around. He was always sitting or lying on the bed.

Whenever butchering was going on at the Ranchito, the poor people of San Juan were always welcome to come up and take home a piece of fresh meat. But not so, Canuto Boronda.

He and Don Manuel had been soldiers together in their boyhood days. Now Canuto and Don Manuel were old men. Whenever Don Manuel thought that Canuto might be out of meat he would order his vaqueros to take not merely a piece of meat down to Canuto. Instead, they were told to drive a young steer down to Boronda's house, butcher it and then hang the whole beef up on Canuto's back porch.

One evening Estolano and his mother happened to be visiting at the adobe house now occupied by the Native Daughters. An old man known as *"El Jarvado,"* meaning the "Hunchback" lived there with his family. His right leg was missing almost up to his body and his left arm had been cut off near the arm pit.

Doctor MacDougall was busy this particular evening amputating the man's remaining leg. He had two women and another man to help him. The bed on which the operation was taking place was in the front room of the house. Beds, in those days, had a large canopy over them, and Estolano could not see what was going on. But he could hear the old man curse and swear at the top of his voice. Estolano was crouched in terror in the far corner of the room. The anesthetic the Doctor was using was large doses of whisky which he administered continually to the patient.

Estolano was insistent on knowing what was going on.

"Mama, what are they doing?"

"They're cutting a man's leg off, dear."

"Then he can't walk any more," persisted Estolano.

"No dear."

"Not unless he can walk on his hands," added Estolano, thoughtfully.

Even Doña Rosario had to smile.

Aunt Pilar also lived on Fourth Street. Her house consisted of six rooms. The back part was pure adobe. The middle section was of mud and stick construction while the front was quite modern, being built of lumber. There were lots of grapes and fruit trees in the backyard.

Estolano and his mother would always stop and visit with Aunt Pilar every Sunday and sometimes even stay over night. Doña Rosario and Madam Pilar were on the friendliest terms. Don Manuel and his sister were always teasing one another. Madam Pilar claimed jokingly that her brother Manuel was lazy and that even the roosters at the Ranchito were slothful, never crowing before ten o'clock in the morning. But Don Manuel was good to his sister, nonetheless, and had given her the lots in San Juan where she lived and had helped her to build her house.

Estolano used to seize every opportunity to get into Aunt Pilar's kitchen, where the pungent odors of the many herbs hanging in bunches from the ceiling delighted his nostrils. He would take long, deep breaths and then ask anxiously: "Aunt Pilar, don't you want me to pick you some more herbs?"

Estolano liked to visit at the Mendoza home. It was at the further end of the Alameda. He and his mother often went there on Sunday. In the summer time, while his mother talked with Doña Louisa, Estolano would slip outside under the apricot trees and gobble down as many ripe, juicy apricots as his little stomach could hold.

The old Mariano Castro house stood at the head of the Alameda. It was a long, spacious adobe house and very roomy. It was every bit as large as the Ranchito where Estolano lived, except that it was only one story high. There were half porches in front and back, the ends of each porch being occupied with a room each.

Dr. Frederick MacDougall was the famous Scotch doctor at Mission San Juan Bautista. He had settled in San Juan shortly after the Gold Rush. He was the first man whom the Spanish people of that Mission town had ever seen who knew how to doctor sick people. All their lives these Mission people had been accustomed to being cared for when they were sick by the old women of the neighborhood. But the days of these old herb doctors was passing. "Don Federico" as he was known to all the Spanish, had a cure for the smallpox which none of the old women of the community possessed.

Taking her little son, Estolano, by the hand, Doña Rosario trudged one hot, sunny afternoon along the dusty road from the Ranchito to the adobe house of Doña Rufina Castro, where Dr. MacDougall lived and had his office.

Little Estolano was not quite sure what it was all about when his mother led him into the presence of the tall Scotch doctor. But "Don Federico" had a way of disarming the fears of little boys even when he was going to hurt them the next instant.

Treating Estolano with all the dignity of a little Don this gentle doctor soon had Estolano's confidence. He casually rolled up the little boy's sleeve. Estolano looked up in wonderment. Estolano felt sure that he had seen a knife in the doctor's hand. To his surprise the doctor deliberately hurt him, just a little bit. Estolano looked down from the face of the doctor to his own little arm and saw a few drops of blood coming. All the while Dr. MacDougall was talking in Spanish. He was keeping Estolano's mind bewildered with stories about horses and bears. Then carefully the doctor pulled Estolano's sleeve back down again.

"There now," he said, *"Esta bien,"* and everything was all over.

Chapter XI

SPANISH SCHOOL

THE WIDE-AWAKE little Estolano clung tightly to his mother's · hand, as early one morning the two crossed the Plaza of Mission San Juan Bautista and continued down the hill to the school for Spanish boys conducted by Señor Hilario Ortez.

Estolano was very excited.

"I want to learn everything that anybody else knows," Estolano informed his mother. He spoke in Spanish for he knew no other language.

Reaching the humble stick and mud schoolhouse, the two paused at the open door.

"Señora Larios!" greeted the elderly school master as he bowed very deferentially.

The wife of the richest and most influential Don in Mission San Juan Bautista said quietly:

"I wish to place my youngest son, Estolano, in your care."

"And this is Estolano?" said Don Hilario as he looked inquiringly at the wide-eyed little boy standing before him. Estolano looked at the strange man not unpleasantly.

"And how old is Don Estolano?" asked the school teacher.

"He is just turning five."

"Plenty old enough to begin learning his letters."

"I know Estolano is going to like your school, Señor Ortez. He could hardly wait for me to finish breakfast, he was so anxious for me to lead the way to your school."

"Learning is a search for a treasure. I hope that he shall find it," said the dignified pedagogue.

"When school is out, you can let Estolano come home alone. He is a smart little fellow and will have no difficulty in making his way back to the Ranchito. *Adios,* Señor Ortez." And Estolano's mother was gone, leaving her son to face the world alone.

Estolano looked around the school at the dozen or more boys of all sizes that were gradually filling the room. All were native Californians and all were speaking Spanish. Estolano was pleased. He had feared that when he went to school everybody would be talking like the Americans, and he would not know a word of what they were saying.

Among the pupils he noticed the three Anzar boys. All were friends of his, he thought. He had seen them at Dr. MacDougall's home. Estolano liked Lupe. And he liked Juan and Anatolio, too. In fact, Estolano was so young that he still liked everybody.

"Now all take your seats and we will start school," said Señor Ortiz. "Don Estolano, you will sit with Don Guadalupe."

Estolano hastened to obey. He was so reassured when Señor Ortiz, too, addressed him in Spanish. He fairly flew to do what he was told.

Señor Ortiz was an old country Spaniard and had been a soldier in California at a time when most of America, even far distant California, was under the rule of Carlos IV of Spain. That was "in the time of the King," the era that the old timers in California were always recalling longingly. Now in his old age Don Hilario was conducting a little school for Spanish boys in a mud and stick house at the foot of the hill below the Plaza.

Don Hilario was a very severe teacher but his pupils progressed well under his instruction. His punishments were those he had learned when a soldier in the army. He had a wooden mallet, smooth on one side and perforated with a dozen holes on the other. If a pupil merited only a slight punishment, such as for having dirty hands, he was given three strokes on the palm of his hand with the smooth side of the mallet. But if the offense merited more severe punishment, as for being tardy or for failure to learn one's lessons, Don Ortiz when the boy held out his hand, would give him three strokes with the perforated side of the mallet. This really hurt. In hard cases where the scholar habitually had dirty hands or too frequently failed to learn his lessons, Don Ortiz would apply such force to the strokes that the perforations from the mallet often raised welts on the boy's hand.

But for grand offenses, such as swearing or fighting, Don Ortiz had a real punishment. It was so severe that but few pupils ever received it. The punishment was called *"Cepo de Campana"* and was that meted out to Spanish soldiers when out on campaigns where confinement in a military prison was not possible.

Señor Ortiz would seat the offending boy on the school room floor and then with a handkerchief would tie his hands together in front of his upraised knees. A round stick about a yard long was next run underneath the boy's knees and above his arms. It was impossible for the boy to stand or to straighten out. The culprit was left to suffer in this position until, the pain becoming unbearable, he would cry out for mercy from the teacher.

A Chilian family lived in one of the apartments rented out along the corridor in the old monastery. At recess these three Chilian boys would often drag Estolano along with them across the Plaza to their home where their mother, like an old bird feeding her young, would stand them up in a row. Estolano along with her own boys, and stuff them with bis-

Chapter XII

APACHE

DOLORES, one of Estolano's older brothers, had just gotten back to the Ranchito from the Vallecitos. He and several other cowboys had driven a band of Don Manuel's cattle to this lush pasture ground and had left them there for the summer.

"Estolano," he called, "come here. I have a present for you." Dolores was removing the large rawhide saddle bags from his pack horse.

Estolano was eager to see what his brother had brought him. "Look in the left saddle bag," said Dolores as he set these leather pouches up against the side of the house. Estolano was a wee bit cautious. He thought he could hear something grunting inside. He listened. Although still somewhat afraid, nevertheless he carefully lifted up the cover of the *alforjas*. There, tucked snugly inside with only its nose in sight was a cute little baby bear!

Vallecitos means "Little Valleys." The *Vallecitos* is a pretty region lying south of the Big Panoche Valley and many miles from the Ranchito. It extends right up to the New Idria quicksilver mine. All along the foothills of the *Vallecitos* the wild oats grew profusely. These were two or three feet high at the time of Dolores' visit. Dolores and another vaquero named Solarzano were making their rounds over the foot hills.

"Look, Dolores. There's a she-bear and two cubs."

At that moment a mother bear with two cubs had just sprung up in the grass in front of them. The old bear immediately began scampering away through the tall grass. She was making her way easily enough but her two little ones were having difficulty trying to keep up.

"Let's catch a cub apiece to take home," suggested Solarzano.

Each of the two horsemen set out to grab a baby bear. Solarzano caught up with his cub first. The little bear was so small, however, and the wild oats were so high that it was impossible for him to use his rope. Quickly Solarzano threw his serape over it and soon had it hopelessly entangled. Then, tying it up without difficulty, he got but few scratches for himself.

Dolores was soon up with his cub, but he likewise was unable to lasso it. So reaching down from his horse he grabbed the little bear by the hind leg. The baby struggled fiercely and tried to scratch and bite. But Dolores held it out at arm's length. The little fellow screamed for dear life, calling to its mother for help. The old bear started after Dolores. But the young cowboy, spurring his horse, put distance as fast as possible between himself and the old bear. Still holding the little bear by the foot he reached camp safely.

A pack horse was rigged up to bring the two little bears to San Juan. Solarzano's prize was loaded into one of the saddle bags. Its snout was tied shut to prevent it from biting, for even when very young cubs are well provided with teeth. The pack horse at first rebelled. It did not like the load being put upon its back and tried to kick the saddle bag off. But after Dolores' cub had been placed in the opposite pocket and the load equalized somewhat, the horse finally went along quietly. The horse walked very gingerly, however, for the first few miles, for it could scent the bears and was somewhat skeptical about having them on his back.

Estolano was delighted with his little bear. As soon as it was taken out of the saddle bag he got some bread and milk which it readily devoured. Dolores put a collar and chain on the little fellow and tied him in a brush shed that stood at the corner of the Patio near the gate. There the little cub thrived and grew. Estolano named him "Apache." He became very gentle. The older boys led him down to the creek a few hundred yards back of the house every day for water. Here the little fellow drank and splashed to his heart's content. When the bear grew large enough, the boys began putting Estolano on its shaggy back, letting him ride "Apache" down to water and back to his quarters. Although he became very tame and quite a pet, Frank and Dolores were always careful to put a muzzle on him before placing Estolano on his back. "Apache" was a grizzly bear. By the time he was two or three years old he had grown to be simply huge in size and, when standing on his hind feet, towered above everyone at the Ranchito.

One Sunday afternoon the Ranchito was full of visiting relatives as usual. The yard was teeming with children, fifteen or twenty of them, besides two baby buggies, each holding a nursling. The older people were in the house. "Apache" was always fastened in one corner of the yard with a chain long enough for him to lumber along as far as the front gate. The children were spinning tops and playing drop the handkerchief. "Apache" was sitting silently on his haunches, moving his head to and fro watching every movement of the children.

Don Manuel had given orders to Dolores and a cowboy named José Espinoza to bring up a nice steer and barbecue it for the guests. The steer, driven by the two cowboys and held by Espinoza's rope around its horns, suddenly caught sight of the crowd of children. It made a wild break to get away.

José Espinoza, in order to check the mad rush of the steer, took several turns of his rope around his saddle horn and set his horse back. The pull was down-hill. To make matters worse Espinoza's saddle cinch was too loose. The hard jerk to stop the steer pulled the saddle, together with Espinoza, right over the horse's head. The steer now loose, and mistakingly thinking that the Patio gate led to freedom, made straight for it.

Estolano and all the children saw the steer coming. They were terrified with fright. None, however, knew which way to run for safety. "Apache," too, saw the steer heading for the yard. He seemed to realize instinctively that the steer was going to trample Estolano and the other children under foot. Planting himself squarely in the middle of the Patio he made ready to protect them. The steer plunged right through the gate into the yard.

"Stop, you brute!" "Apache" seemed to be saying as he blocked the way of the steer. "I'll not let you trample on these children."

"Apache" seized the steer by the head. By main strength, with one paw on each horn he forced down the animal's head until the steer's lower jaw rested flatly on the ground. "Apache" continued to hold the steer fast until all the children had escaped to safety and the two mothers had rescued their babies. Then with a terrific growl, as if to say: "Go, you rascal!" he turned the steer loose. The frightened animal ran through the yard and out one of the side gates.

Estolano and all the other children were soon back in the yard playing as noisily as ever. "Apache" they rewarded by bringing him a comb of honey. To the delight of the children the happy, smiling bear, sitting on his haunches and holding the square of honey in his two paws, ate as though enjoying a real feast.

"No, no, 'Apache'," laughed the youngsters from time to time, "You have had enough. Too much honey makes people sick." But "Apache," licking his chops, kept begging all the afternoon for more.

A few months after "Apache's" heroic deed, he gained for himself a few hours of freedom. His chain wore in two near the collar, and one night he stole away. He wandered to a blackberry patch near the Vergeles Ranch at Natividad. "Apache" was enjoying himself so much. It was the first time since he was a cub that he had ever known what it was to be free. And the berries tasted so good. A young man was coming. But "Apache" was unafraid of people. No one had ever harmed him. The young man pointed a long stick or something at him.

"Bang!"

"Apache's" brain burst. His body crumped in a heap on the ground. The indifferent young man sauntered slowly over to the lifeless body.

"Why, this is no wild bear!" exclaimed the young man in astonishment. He examined the collar around the dead bear's neck. Instantly he realized: "I've killed somebody's pet."

The neighbor boy brought the collar over to the Ranchito to see if it indeed was "Apache" that he had killed. When Estolano recognized the collar and was told that "Apache" was dead, he burst into tears. He was furious for a time to think that he was powerless to aid "Apache" in any way. Later he silently hung the collar over the door of the brush house that had been "Apache's" home almost as long as Estolano could remember. As he left the vacant doorway the emptiness of the little house seemed reflected in Estolano's very heart. There the emptyness was greater than in the brush hut itself.

The Ranchita Preparing for the Fiesta and Bull Fight

Chapter XIII

VISITORS AT THE RANCHITO

There was an old, old man who often visited at the Ranch-ito. He was tall and slender with white hair and beard. He walked with a staff instead of a cane. He was a regular old country Spaniard. The children of the Ranchito were all afraid of him. If he asked one of them to do something for him and the child didn't obey instantly the old man's staff would surely come down on the head of the unlucky youngster. His name was Guadalupe Cantua, and he lived with his daughter at the Carnadero south of Gilroy.

One afternoon he was sitting out on the porch at the Ranch-ito. He asked Estolano to get him a light for his cigarette. Matches were almost unknown in those days, and when a child was sent for a light he was expected to bring a lighted stick from the fireplace or a coal of fire. Estolano ran to the kitchen. Instead of taking an old spoon or something of that sort to carry a coal of fire to the old gentleman, Estolano in a spirit of mischief simply picked up a tiny coal of fire and tossing it up and down in order to keep it from burning his hand brought it to the old man. This trifling on the part of Estolano irritated Cantua. He seized Estolano's wrist and held it firmly while he leisurely lit his cigarette. Estolano squirmed and hollered and finally pulled away, but not before the coal had burned a nice little blister in the palm of his hand.

The Ranchito became a sort of stopping place for most of the miners on foot going through the country on their way to the *placieres*. The house was on the main road from Monterey to San Juan. People, seeing the big house beside the road, seemed attracted to it. No doubt it suggested to them that there were lots of good eats there. In this they were not mistaken. Don Manuel made every visitor welcome.

Some of these miners stayed two or three days. Others remained as long as two or three weeks. If they had pitched in and helped with the work on the Ranchito and had made themselves generally agreeable, Don Manuel, when they were ready to resume their travel, would usually give them some old plug of a horse that was too old to be of further use in driving cattle. There were lots of old saddles around the Ranchito, and he would make them a present of a saddle as well. One time an American on his way to the mines stayed quite a while. On his leaving he was of course given a horse and saddle. Sometime later he came back from the mines with his pockets filled with gold. He wanted to pay Don Manuel.

"I am offended, señor," snorted the old Don. "The idea of you offering me money for my hospitality!"

An old Frenchman on one occasion stopped for several days. He was a sort of watchmaker. While there he overhauled and repaired the two hand organs in the *sala*. In the course of time some of the little dancers on the Santa Ana organ had got broken off. This old Frenchman fixed them back on again. He also put the other hand organ in good order.

On his way to the *placieres* another Frenchman also stayed over a few days. When he got ready to go on his way, he likewise was given an old plug and saddle. He was so grateful that he insisted on making a present of his finely trained French pointer dog to Estolano and the other children. It was a well-bred dog, black with large ears. This dog understood only French. Before the Frenchman left he taught the children the

French commands. *"Allez coucher,"* meant "Go and lie down," *"Apportez ici,"* "Bring it here," *"Allez chercher,"* "Go and look for," *"Allez d'hors,"* "Get out doors," *"Vic,"* "Come here."

The dog's name was "Touto." He lived to be a very old dog. One of the children's games at the Ranchito was "Ante over." This was played by throwing a solid rubber ball over the roof of the house. Touto could catch the ball better than any of the youngsters. He would watch the ball coming and catch it on the first bound. This was allowable in the game and counted the same as a direct catch. The children were all anxious to have first choice in the game. They all wanted Touto on their side. Touto was always the first "person" chosen. He was as much a player in the game as any of the children. Touto had other tricks also. A person could give him one end of a sack, and if the person was strong enough he could swing Touto around in a circle. Touto would never let go of the sack as long as anybody was trying to take it away from him.

There was another dog at the Ranchito that also lived to be very old. It was a mastiff and was called "Watch." It was poisoned twice. One night it attacked a drunken Indian who was prowling around the Ranchito, tearing the Indian's arm quite severely. Later someone poisoned the dog, and it was suspected that the Indian did it. The dog did not die, however. Estolano's brother, Frank, who owned the dog, cut off the tips of its ears and the end of its tail in order to keep the blood circulating. He also gave Watch oil to drink and he got all right. Another time this same dog was poisoned, and they cut off some more of his ears and made his tail a little shorter. Watch could be sent alone to drive cattle out of a corn field. He was so strong that he could catch cows by the tail, like he was "tailing" them, and almost throw them down.

Don Manuel Larios and Don José Abrego, of Monterey, were great friends. Abrego had been the revenue officer in that coast city for many years under the Mexican regime. The Abre-

Chapter XIV

CHINA MARBLES

ON SUNDAY AFTERNOON in summertime Estolano's brother, Tony, would often wander up the creek to one of the Indian cabins where he would play "Cunquian" with Rosario for fifty cents an ante. "Come along, Estolano," said Tony one afternoon. "I'm going up to Rosario and Felipa's. It will be a nice walk for you." Estolano was only too anxious to be going somewhere—anywhere—and immediately he fell into step along side of his big brother.

Rosario and Felipa's cabin had only two rooms, one a bed room and the other a larger room that served as kitchen, dining room and sitting room. Gathering around the kitchen table the two men soon began their game.

Estolano, child-like, kept walking around looking at every-thing in Felipa's house and finally wandered into the bedroom. On a bench stood Felipa's trunk. It was wide open and there, lying on top in plain sight, were five coins, all half dollar pieces.

"Gee, what a lot of money!" thought Estolano. "I wonder if Felipa would know it if I took one of them." But instead of taking only one coin as he had originally intended, the temp-tation was too much for him, and he grabbed up all five of them. Quickly thrusting them in his pocket he returned quietly to the living room, endeavoring all the while not to attract any more attention to himself than possible. The house suddenly seemed oppressive to him, like it was going to crush him. He felt a great urge to get out of doors and get away. Once outside he hurried up the little dry gulch back of the house. All the while his little brain was scheming how he could hide the money and not get caught with it. He was wearing a pair of homemade pants that were lined on the inside.

As soon as he was safely out of sight he took his pocket knife and ripped open one of the seams a tiny bit. One at a time he let the coins slide down inside the lining. He spaced the coins so evenly around the knee that no one would ever suspect that there were any coins there. Then he went back into the house and calmly began watching the game.

"That's twice now I beat you, Rosario," laughed Tony. "Want to play any more?"

Rosario told Felipa, his wife, to bring him some more money. "Tony has cleaned me."

Felipa hastened into the bedroom to get the money from the trunk. Coming back into the living room her face was long. She wore a surprised, hurt look.

"The money that was in my trunk is gone, Rosario. *No hay dinero!*"

Suspicion fell at once on Estolano. He had been seen wandering around in the bedroom only a short time before. Next he had been seen going up the little gulch back of the house. Estolano's brother, who was also his godfather in confirmation, was deeply perplexed. In order to give his little brother a chance to get out of his predicament, if in truth he had stolen the money, Tony suggested to Estolano that they should take a little walk.

"Maybe the pack rats have carried off the money up the gulch, and we can find it."

Estolano cheerfully accompanied his brother. He had the

coins so securely hidden that he felt sure even if his brother searched him he would not find them. He walked brazenly out of the house.

At every gopher hole they came to Tony would tell Estolano to look carefully down into it and see if perhaps the money was there. At the same time he would walk on ahead of Estolano with his back turned. He wanted to give his little brother a chance to return the money. He hoped that Estolano would drop the coins down in the hole and then cry out: "Why here is the money right in this gopher hole!"

But Estolano had no intention of giving up the money. Although he helped Tony look everywhere, of course the money was not found and the two went back into the cabin. Immediately the two Indians came right out openly and accused Estolano of having taken the money. They grabbed him roughly and began searching him from head to foot and in every pocket. At last the mystified Indians and the perplexed Tony gave up their search. All felt certain that Estolano was the thief. But the straight-faced little boy completely outwitted them.

The loss of the money broke up the game for the afternoon, and Tony and his little brother set out for the Ranchito. As soon as supper was over and it was good and dark Estolano slipped unobserved out of the house and made his way back of the big adobe corral. Along a fence at the sixth post hole from the corral he buried his loot. Now he breathed a sigh of relief. With the money no longer on his person he felt absolutely safe.

A day or two later Frank Rojas from the San Joaquin Ranch came riding over to the Ranchito to visit. He was a great friend of Estolano's brothers, Frank and Dolores. The three young men were spending the afternoon lounging about the corral and boasting of their cleverness in riding horses and roping cattle.

"But do you know," declared Dolores, "Our little brother Estolano is the cleverest of us all. He is a natural born thief. Not only steals but is so shrewd that he can't be caught."

Dolores then went on to tell of the mysterious disappearance of the five half-dollar pieces at the Indian's cabin the other Sunday. "We are dead sure that Estolano got away with the money all right, but we can't catch him. He is too shrewd and clever. Tony and the Indians searched him and did everything to find it, but they couldn't get the least inkling as to where he has the money."

"Well," suggested Frank Rojas, "let's put up a game on the little rascal."

"But how?"

"The kid likes marbles, doesn't he?"

"Sure. He's a regular little gambler with marbles."

"Well, then," said Rojas. "Suppose I make a bargain with Estolano. I'll offer to sell him fifty cents worth of marbles. That will make him produce one of the fifty cent pieces. You fellows watch close and you will discover where he keeps the money."

"Oh, Estolano," shouted Dolores as they saw the little brother playing near the house. "Come here. Rojas has something for you."

The unsuspecting Estolano came running to see what Rojas was going to give him.

"See here, Estolano. I've got more marbles than I know what to do with at home and I thought you might like to have some of them."

"Sure," spoke up Estolano promptly.

"Well now I want to sell some of them. I have one hundred pure China marbles, and I'm willing to sell them to you for fifty cents. Isn't that a real bargain?"

"Sure. I'll take them," declared Estolano at once.

"No trust, remember," said Rojas firmly. "I'll have to have the money."

"Sure," declared Estolano.

"Well then I'll ride home and get the marbles. You have your money ready when I get back." With that Rojas jumped on his horse and rode away at a stiff gallop down the road from the Ranchito into San Juan.

Estolano, instead of going back to the house, ambled leisurely around back of the adobe corral out of sight of his brothers who were busy with their horses. Coming eventually to the sixth post in the fence, he carelessly scraped with his foot at the bottom of the post, at the same time gazing unconcernedly at the distant mountains. Glancing down occasionally he saw that he had uncovered one of the coins. Bending down quickly like a hawk pouncing on a chicken he grabbed up the coin. He then walked on slowly a short distance farther. Calmly turning around he looked to see if anyone was watching him. All the world was serene and quiet. Not a person was in sight. Walking quickly he was soon back at the house with the fifty cent piece safely in his pocket.

So anxious was Estolano to get his hands on those one hundred China marbles that he was already out at the gate beside the road waiting for Rojas when he rode up.

"There, Estolano," spoke up Rojas, cheerily. "Here are your marbles. A hundred of them. Count them." And he tossed a cloth sack of marbles down to the waiting buyer.

Estolano hung on tight to his four bit piece until he had counted the marbles and found the number to be correct. Then he handed the coin to Rojas who turned on his horse and rode away down the road back to San Juan.

Don Manuel wouldn't believe a word of it when Frank and Dolores told him that Estolano was getting to be a regular little thief. "You'll have to prove it," declared the old Don. Tony had already told him of the lost coins of the previous Sunday.

"Children, of course, often take things that they think they want to play with," declared Don Manuel to Frank and Dolores. "You have to make allowances for that. But as to stealing money, Estolano is too honest a boy to do anything like that."

"But we can prove it," declared Dolores. "Here are four of the coins. Frank Rojas has the other one. Estolano bought a hundred marbles with it from Rojas."

"Where did you get these four coins??" asked Don Manuel, very judiciously.

"While Estolano was waiting at the gate for Rojas, we went to the sixth post from the corral where we had watched Estolano digging with his foot. We dug a little more and uncovered the other four."

Estolano enjoyed playing with his new marbles all the rest of the afternoon. He was practising to become a perfect shot. "I'll clean out all the boys in town. They aren't going to beat me any more." Estolano shot and shot knocking out the last of the hundred marbles from the circle without missing a single shot. "All I need," mused Estolano, "is to have the first shot and I'll clean them out without their ever getting a turn to play."

At supper Estolano was very bragadocio. He felt himself rich. "I not only own one hundred fine marbles," he thought to himself, "but I have four half dollars in cash safely hidden away where no one can ever find them."

"Estolano, come to my room," ordered Don Manuel after supper as the family arose from the table. "You, too, Patrocinio."

Estolano was frightened. He became more and more uneasy as he and his brother, Patrocinio, sat down on the lounge in their father's room. "Has anyone told father about the Indian money?" he asked himself. Things were plainly getting out of control, and Estolano's little brain was working feverishly as he tried to think up just what move he would make next.

"Stealing," said Don Manuel, speaking to the two boys slowly, "is something that no people will tolerate. A person can do all sorts of things that harm only himself and usually get by with them. But when it comes to injuring another person, there is no hope of escape. Stealing injures another. A thief is a coward. A thief is hated by everybody."

Don Manuel's words came like sledge hammer blows.

"Estolano, you are a thief! It is my duty as your father to do everything in my power while you are still young to break you from stealing."

Estolano looked to his brother as if for help.

"Patrocinio," ordered Don Manuel, "get down on your hands and knees."

Estolano was alarmed lest his father was going to punish Patrocinio for what he had done. He was just on the point of shouting that he was the guilty person and not Patrocinio.

"Now Estolano, take off your pants."

There was a moment of utter futility as Estolano did as his father told him.

"Climb on Patrocinio's back."

As Estolano did so Patrocinio gripped both of Estolano's hands firmly under his chin and held his younger brother firmly.

"This," said Don Manuel, "is the method used to bring rebellious Spanish soldiers to their senses. I hope it will do as much for you." With a quirt Don Manuel struck Estolano a terrific blow. Estolano gave a terrible scream. At the same moment he bit his brother so savagely on the back of the neck Patrocinio almost let him get away

"Patrocinio," shouted Don Manuel, "if you let Estolano get away I will give you the punishment instead."

Patrocinio held Estolano tighter than ever while two more strokes were administered with all of Don Manuel's might.

Estolano was allowed to wander off to bed. In all the house-

Chapter XV

SCHOOL DAYS

AFTER TWO YEARS, when Don Hilario Ortiz had closed his school for Spanish boys, Estolano was sent to the American public school. Here all the common children of San Juan went to school.

In this public school everyone talked English. Estolano, who knew no language but Spanish, was greatly bewildered for a time. He had to begin going to school all over again. First he had to learn to talk English. It was not long, however, until he had mastered the language of the play yard and was right at home among the American children.

But his school work did not go so well. He had no difficulty in learning the English alphabet, but he experienced great difficulty in learning to read English words. In trying to read, he would give the same sound to the vowels in the English words that he had learned to give them in reading Spanish. Each vowel in Spanish has practically only one sound. But in reading English he found that the five English vowels have as many as twenty-seven different pronunciations. Finally Estolano gave up trying to fit his Spanish knowledge into the learning of English. He simply learned to pronounce arbitrarily each individual English printed word.

Practically all the buildings around San Juan were of adobe. But the public schoolhouse was built of lumber. Instead of the walls being two or three feet thick, Estolano was surprised to find that they were only a few inches thick. The schoolhouse itself was about sixty feet long and maybe half as wide. It was located over the line from the town on hand that belonged to the Ranchito. Estolano's father had donated about two acres for the use of the school.

The schoolhouse consisted of only one room. There were two teachers. Miss Kimball had charge of the beginners. She occupied the south end of the building. In her part of the room the walls were covered with large pasteboard charts. Some had the alphabet in capital letters. Others had the alphabet in small print. Still other charts contained words of one syllable like bat, cat, hat, mat, rat and so on. There was also a chart with all the colors of the rainbow on it. The little boys and girls were required to repeat the names of all the primary colors until they knew them by heart. The north end of the school room was occupied by the older scholars and was presided over by Mr. Shearer, the head of the school.

Mr. Shearer had ways of instilling knowledge into the densest numbskull and doing it insidiously. He used the singing method. He had various tunes which he would teach the pupils to sing instead of the songs in the usual school song books. One of his songs was for learning the names of the states of the Union. After many repetitions the pupils would get the song by heart and with it the names of all the states. When this song had been well learned he would bring forth another one giving the state capitals. Then followed a song composed of the names of the counties of California. Before closing school he would have them sing the multiplication table. This would start out with Once one is one, two times two are four, three times three are nine, four times four are sixteen. The chorus was to the tune of Yankee Doodle:

Five times five are twenty-five,
And five times six are thirty.

Five times seven are thirty-five
And five times eight are forty.

Acquiring knowledge in this manner was without effort and Estolano and the other pupils thought it fun.

Each Friday afternoon the pupils were required to recite a little piece of poetry that had been given them during the week to memorize. On those Friday entertainments there were also recitations, spelling matches and singing.

There were no grades in school. A pupil was ranked according to the reader he was in. *Wilson's Readers* were in use. In the spelling matches all the pupils, for instance, in the Second Reader were allowed to choose sides and spell down until only one pupil was left. Then those in the Third Reader and so on to the Sixth.

Estolano was fairly good in reading but not so in spelling. He never stood up very long. Two or three rounds and he was spelled down and had to take his seat. One reason, perhaps, why Estolano was not a good speller was because during the week when his spelling class would recite, he would cut out the spelling lesson from his spelling book and carry it to class with him. The pupils had to stand up with their arms folded. When it came Estolano's turn to spell a word he would look down humbly, and there snugly in the palm of his right hand would lie the little slip ready to prompt him if necessary. But in the spelling matches Estolano had to stand on his own feet, and he was soon on his way to his seat.

Games of all kinds were played in the school yard. Baseball was unknown at that time. But in its place they played what was called Town Ball. They also played "Come, come, pull away." The smaller boys occupied their time with marbles, tops and Mumbly Peg. The little girls had also their games of "Ring Around a Posy" and drop the handkerchief.

Water for drinking had to be carried to the school in buckets from a distance of three blocks. Each bucket was supplied with a dipper, and when the water would arrive the pupils would form in line, each shouting, "I'm next! I'm next!" but this did them no good. All had to await their turn.

The road to school was straight down from the Ranchito to the schoolhouse. Estolano seldom played "hookey." But one day when he got to the Ranchito fence, instead of going along to school, he switched off to the right a little bit and wandered into an orchard belonging to a man by the name of George Chalmers. Continuing on to the edge of town, he met several children he knew. He stayed with them and gambled for marbles all day long. About four o'clock when he saw the pupils from the public school going home he made tracks for the Ranchito. No one at home knew but what he had been to school all day.

Having once got started playing "hookey," Estolano liked it so well that he kept right on. He was absent from school three days in succession. The third afternoon, instead of going home by way of the orchard, he walked boldly past the schoolhouse. He was going along whistling and all unconcerned. As he passed the schoolhouse door, Mr. Shearer called to him. Estolano walked brazenly into the room. "Take off your jacket and kneel down," ordered Mr. Shearer. Estolano did so. Mr. Shearer had a nice apple switch which he laid three separate times with all his strength across Estolano's back. Estolano wept with pain and rage. That cured Estolano of playing 'hookey." He never gave Mr. Shearer an opportunity to use his apple switch on him again.

"Testerosas" was a game that the boys of the school went in for a great deal. It was in imitation of the Spanish sport of Testerosas indulged in by horsemen on such feast days as San Juan's Day and Santa Ana's Day. It was a very rough sport. Men mounted on their best saddle horses would line up facing each other and then charge in an endeavor to drive their opponent's line back. The sport is indulged in furiously and often-

times a skillful horseman mounted on a strong horse would come against his opponent so hard that he would knock both horse and rider down. Not infrequently the rider and horse were hurt. But that was part of the game and no one had any right to complain. At the public school the larger boys would be the horses. Each one would pick a small boy for his rider and carry him on his back. Estolano was always much in demand for he was small and very active. He usually rode for either Cassius Crooks or Isaac Mylar. The game was played recklessly. The boys playing horses would hurl themselves and their riders with all their strength at their opponents, knocking them right and left. The wonder is that there never were any broken bones or other serious injuries.

While Estolano was attending public school, the Civil War was raging and troops were stationed in San Juan. The war spread even to the school children. The larger boys organized themselves into companies of "Secessionists" and "Black Republicans." Every noon the two armies repaired to the Larios field adjoining the school grounds and there fought it out with rocks and whatever other missiles were at hand. Some of the officers had swords carved out of wood and often fought duels to decide the day's struggle.

During the battles the younger lads like Estolano were kept in the rear carrying ammunition in the form of rocks to the front. On one occasion when Estolano had delivered a handkerchief full of rocks to the front line he accidentally stepped into a mud hole. Quick as a flash Estolano scooped up a handful of the soft mud and let drive at the "Sesesh" flag. He made a perfect bull's eye hit and smeared the flag beautifully. The color bearer stepped instantly to the front and challenged the evil-doer to personal combat.

A fighting Catalonian like Estolano couldn't let pass a challenge like that. He stepped forward immediately. The Captains of the two armies then agreed that the two boys should fight it out and that the outcome should decide the battle for the day.

Estolano's opponent was Nathan Mount. He was two or three years older than Estolano but not any larger. The two struck a few blows. Estolano quickly saw that his opponent was his superior with his fists. So Estolano decided to grapple with him. Nathan was wearing a little red handkerchief around his neck. Estolano got hold of it and began twisting fast and furiously, at the same time tripping Nathan with his foot. Both fell to the ground. One lick was all that Estolano was able to get in, but he made Nathan's nose bleed. Nathan was much stronger and more wiry and soon had Estolano lying flat on his back. He covered up his face with his hands and arms as best he could while Nathan rained blow after blow on his head.

"Give up?"

"No!"

The blows continued. Estolano's head was being beaten severely. Try as hard as he could he was unable to get out from under Nathan.

At that moment the bell for school rang. The two Captains agreed to call the battle a tie.

It was three days before Estolano was able to return to school.

There was going to be a big fiesta at the neighboring Ranchito. It was Don Manuel's birthday. Estolano's father, who was always lavish in his hospitality, decided that he wanted all the school children to attend the party. Many were his grand children living at the Ranchito. Early in the morning he sent a

messenger over to the school house to tell Mr. Shearer to dismiss school for the day and for all to come over to the Ranchito as his guests.

"Who does this man Larios think he is?" exploded Mr.

Shearer. "We don't close American schools for birthday parties. You tell Mr. Larios I said positively No!"

The boy went back to the Ranchito and reported what the American teacher had said.

"Get me my horse!" Don Manuel ordered. "Get me my riata!"

Don Manuel rode straight to the schoolhouse. Without getting off his horse he rode right up to the entrance and slapped his riata against the door by way of knocking.

"Come out here, Shearer," he ordered. "I want to talk to you."

The teacher came to the door.

"Shearer," said the old Don firmly, "I want you and the other teacher, Miss Kimball, and all the children to spend the day at the Ranchito with me and help celebrate my birthday."

"No!" said Shearer positively. "I will not dismiss school for a birthday party. Americans don't do that sort of thing."

Don Manuel straightened up to his full height in his saddle. "Then in that case," he thundered, "I will take things into my own hands. This school house, you know, is on my land. If you don't come to my party and bring these children with you I will get help, and we'll drag this schoolhouse right out into the middle of the road. We will leave you and your schoolhouse sitting nowhere."

The American school teacher began to realize why Don Manuel was known everywhere in San Juan as the "King of the Dons."

"We don't want to have any trouble, Mr. Larios," said Shearer beginning to weaken. He paused for a moment. "I guess it will be all right to close school for one day. Yes," he said finally, "we will all come."

The children were delighted. They all knew that it meant feasting and a day of playing games at Don Manuel's house. The principal called all the children outside the school building and formed them in procession. Then with himself and Miss Kimball in the rear, the whole school followed Don Manuel, riding in triumph back to the Ranchito.

Chapter XVI

THE FUTURE LAWYER

AN OLD INDIAN named Remijio lived at the Paradon, an Indian village about two miles north of San Juan. He would come riding along on a burro with only a short stick to guide it. He used to ride this little donkey to church at the old Mission every Sunday morning and leave it tied up at the hitching rail in front of the corridors. Estolano and several other little boys would often appropriate the animal while the old Indian was in church. No less than four or five would get on the burro at one time. They would even perch on its neck. Someone would give the burro a prod and away he would go on a trot. They always rode in the direction of the National Hotel. When the burro would become weary, he would suddenly throw down his head and stop abruptly. This would send the whole string of boys sliding over the donkey's head into the dust. But they would get right up and climb back on again. Estolano and the other little boys thought it great sport.

When Don Manuel's cousin, José Antonio, came up from Mexico for a visit at the Ranchito, he brought a small French music box as a present for Estolano. It wound up with a key like a clock and played half a dozen tunes. Among these was the *Marseillaise.* As this music box was very small, Estolano would often put it in his shirt bosom and take it to Mass with him. After the services he would stand around very innocently among the corridor arches and start it playing. The music sounded clear, but a long ways off. Estolano enjoyed watching the mystified looks on the faces of his boy friends as they listened, never suspecting that it was Estolano who was fooling them.

At a christening in the old Mission the *padrones,* or sponsors, upon leaving the church, were usually met at the head of the corridors by hosts of boys who demanded the *"bolo"* or gift from the padrino. It was then the duty of the padrino to reach into his pockets and toss out silver coins to the crowd. When Estolano was still a small boy he and his mother stood sponsors for a child belonging to Manuel Buelna and his wife. Estolano's father had given him a twenty dollar gold piece for the *bolo.* It required quite a bit of hustling for Estolano to change this into silver coins but he finally succeeded and when the time came he was ready for the fray. At the head of the corridors the boys started hollering "Bolo, Padrino!" Estolano reached into his bulging pants pockets and began throwing out dimes by the handful. He got a great kick out of watching the boys scramble for the coins. Whenever the excitement would die down, he would throw out another handful. By the time he got to the end of the corridors all of his two hundred dimes were gone!

Bishop Alemany was a Spanish priest and was a great friend of Don Manuel. Whenever the Bishop was in San Juan he always visited at the Ranchito. Don Manuel and the Bishop were sitting in the *sala* smoking their cigars when Estolano happened in from school. He was promptly called to meet the Bishop. Then Don Manuel urged his little son to mount the large family dining room table and make a speech to show the Bishop how well he was progressing at the English school. Estolano got up and recited the little piece of poetry he had learned for school just the Friday before. It was:

"One, two, three, four, five,
I caught a hare alive.
Six, seven, eight, nine, ten,
I let it go again."

The Bishop was very pleased. "Now," said Don Manuel, "give it to us in Spanish."

Like a flash Estolano started with:

"Uno, dos, tres, cuatro, cinco,
Agarro una liebre—

When he came to the word "viva," alive, Estolano realized instantly that it would not rhyme with "cinco." Almost by inspiration he changed it to "brinco," meaning to jump.

— — — — — al brinco,
Seis, siete, ocho, nueve, diez.
La dejo ir otra vez."

The Bishop sprang to his feet and seized Estolano in his arms.

"That couldn't be better," he exclaimed.

Turning to Don Manuel he said:

"Your little son has the making of a very smart man. See to it, Don Manuel, that he becomes a lawyer!"

Riding the Fiesta Bull

Chapter XVII

"THEM DAYS WAS NICE"

NOTHING SOUNDS SO NICE as a serenade. A person wakes up to the sound of sweet music. On their birthdays everyone at the Ranchito was given a serenade. Even the youngest babes, when they reached a year in age were serenaded, for it gave an excuse for a party. A violin and a guitar were the musical instruments employed. Sometimes a flute would be added, but only for special occasions.

Juan Antonio Higuera and his family lived over the hill two miles from the Ranchito house. Even this was not too far away for the serenaders. The start from the Ranchito house would be half an hour before midnight. Some would walk and some rode horseback. The crowd would arrive by one o'clock. Doña Louisa was a wonderful cake maker and always had a big batch of cookies and cakes waiting.

The time for a serenade is between midnight and two o'clock in the morning. The serenaders always tried to get as near as possible to the window of the person whose birthday was being celebrated. When all had arrived under the window a good singer gave the salutation. This was a beautiful little ditty set to a dreamy, melodious air. It was more inclined to make one sleep than to wake a person up.

After this song there would follow a lively tune by the musicians. Presently the door was thrown open and the crowd poured into the house. There was always good cheer as well as good eats awaiting them. The younger people danced throughout the night. When broad daylight came all departed for their homes. Birthday presents were unknown. The serenade itself was the gift.

Christmas presents were likewise unheard of at the Ranchito, and Santa Claus was unknown. But all parents saw to it that their children had new clothes from head to foot for the Midnight Mass on Christmas eve. These were all bought beforehand but were never worn before this particular night.

Don Manuel used to make a special trip to San Francisco each year just before Christmas. He would come home loaded with boxes of oranges, bunches of bananas and clothes for everybody at the Ranchito. There were suits for the youngest boy up to the grown sons. For the women and girls there were hats, shawls and dress goods by the bolt.

At the Ranchito there was always music and dancing as well as feasting on Christmas Eve. A game that was played in many a San Juan home as well as the Ranchito at that time was called *Rifa de Compadres.* Only boys and young girls took part. Two scribes were appointed. The man took down all the girls' names and the woman those of the young men. Each name was written on a strip of paper, rolled up tightly and dropped into a dish, the names of the men in one container and those of the girls in another. Then a little girl would draw out a name from the men's dish, while a little boy would draw one from the girls' dish. These were handed to the judge who would read off the two names and announce that they were Compadres. This meant that the boy and the girl were to stand up, walk to the center of the room, shake hands, put their arms around one another and give each other a kiss. Estolano enjoyed these games immensely, At eleven o'clock the party would end with every one setting out in their new togs to walk to Midnight Mass at the Mission Church.

On Sundays the Ranchito was always full to overflowing. Immediately after Mass all the Larios and the Higuera families would congregate at the Ranchito. With those already living there the house was certainly running over full. Among the visitors were Martina and Melicio with their family of five or six youngsters. José Maria came with as many more. Juan Antonio Higuera, the violinist, always brought his family. Josefa de German and Refugio Larios de Carlos also came with their flocks of little boys and girls. Even the members of the family living at Santa Ana would come and spend the day. The latter would remain all night, taking all day Monday in getting back to the ranch.

The regular picnic grounds were down by the creek under some willows. Each Sunday a yearling heifer would be driven down there, butchered and then barbecued for the crowd. Tortillas, a big pan of Chili sauce, barbecued meat and wine made up the meal. The rest of the afternoon was given over to games and visiting.

Every Sunday night there was dancing. All the families would gather in the *sala.* Candles burned along the walls in profusion. All was gaiety. The music consisted of guitars, violins and sometimes a harp. Don Manuel was never so happy as when making other people happy.

Juan Barcelon was a great dancer. He was from Hermosillo, Mexico, and was the husband of Estolano's sister, Alta Gracia Higuera. He had a dance called the "Coyote." It had its own special music. People would hold their sides from laughter as he imitated the cunning, slithering movements of a coyote. When the music stopped he would stand perfectly still for a moment and then howl like a coyote. This would bring forth tumultous applause.

José Espinoza was the Larios cowboy from Santa Barbara. He could whistle like a mocking bird and loud enough for people to dance to his whistling. He often whistled for the dancers

Chapter XVIII

ALWAYS ON THE GO

Don Manual Larios and Señor Abrego of Monterey owned the first family carriages ever landed in California. Whenever an English ship from around the Horn was due to arrive in Monterey, Abrigo would send word to Don Manuel. The latter would promptly start a string of *carretas* loaded with soap, hides and tallow for the port of Monterey, where Don Manuel would be right on hand to see what goods or other effects he could trade for. In this way he obtained his carriage and his old Grandfather clock. More than once the Abrego family visited the Ranchito in their carriage. Likewise the Larios family visited the Abregos in Monterey. Nor were these just afternoon calls. A visit of a week or so was considered quite proper.

The Larios family had many other friends as well as relatives in Monterey beside the Abregos. They often visited at the Doña Chica Garner home. She had a very large two-story adobe building very close to the beach in Monterey. She was the mother of José Garner, a brilliant attorney. Doña Chica also had two daughters, Clothilde, married, and Lucretia, single. The latter was very beautiful. Aunt Pilar's daughter, Crecentia, was married and also lived in Monterey. The Larios family would visit at her home.

On a trip around the beach in their carriage the Larios family once saw a young whale calf stranded on the beach. It was about thirty-five or forty feet long and away over Estolano's head in height. On the north side of the wharf as the Larios family was returning home they saw a crowd of whalers rendering out whale oil. The stench was so strong and sickening that they had to drive past as quickly as possible. The sailors were feasting on the cracklings from the whale blubber.

Santa Cruz was another place the Larios family visited. The first day from San Juan they would stop over night at a ranch on a big lake called *Laguna de las Calabazas* (Pumpkin Lake). There was supposed to be a sea monster in this lake. At least the old folks talked a great deal about it. This may have been to keep the youngsters from going near the water. There were two boys at this house and Estolano soon got on friendly terms with them. They all went out to play, but not in the direction of the lake. They went up the hill away from it among the redwoods and gathered gum from the trees to chew. Instead of being pink or reddish like the gum from pine trees this was of a yellow color.

In Santa Cruz Estolano's father and mother both had sisters. His mother's sister was Chinita, married to Juan Perez. They had about ten children. Don Manuel's sister was Maria Antonia, married to Jésus Amaya. The Amaya family was about twelve in number. There was a beautiful willow grove on the banks of the San Lorenzo River a hundred yards from the Perez house where the Larios family were staying. The Perez and the Amaya families got together and gave a big barbecue in this grove in honor of their visiting relatives from San Juan.

Estolano's cousin, Manuel Perez, and he were sleeping together. Manuel's brother was married to Juliana German of San Juan. They lived on the northwest side across the town from the Perez home which was on the extreme east side. Juliana's younger sister was getting married at Juliana's home. Although the bride to be was about ten years older than Estolano yet he fondly imagined that she was a sweetheart of his.

"Pistola," as Manuel was nicknamed, whispered to Estolano as they lay there in bed that he had a saddle nag in the stable. He proposed that he and Estolano should get up quietly, saddle the horse and go to the wedding. The two boys arrived just in time to witness the wedding ceremony and to enjoy the subsequent feast. There were lots of good eats and also a few caresses and kisses for Estolano from the bride.

When Don Manuel moved from the Santa Ana Ranch to the Ranchito he rented the Santa Ana for a term of years to Frank Lynch, an Irishman from San Francisco who could speak good Spanish. Later Don Manuel made a visit to the home of Mr. Lynch in San Francisco. The Larios family drove to San Jose in the family carriage, Estolano, his father and mother and his brother, Patrocinio. From San Jose they took a stage to Alviso on the southern end of the Bay of San Francisco. Here they went on board a small steamer bound for the city. On the steamer deck there was a life-saver suspended by a rope from the beam above. It was just low enough for Estolano to reach. As he was tugging at the rope his hat fell off and the wind carried it over the railing and into the rolling waters of the Bay. Estolano had no extra hat, and so he arrived in the city bareheaded. He was terribly mortified, for in those days no one ever thought of going bareheaded in public.

In the city the family stopped at the California House. It was located on Pine Street where the Gaillard Hotel is now. Estolano was down with his father in the billiard room sitting by a large plate glass window. A man was talking to Don Manuel and playing with Estolano. He did something that caused Estolano to throw his head back. He hit the window so hard that it shattered the whole pane. It did not cut Estolano's head, but it made his head ache for quite a spell. Don Manuel had to pay for having the glass replaced.

While staying at this hotel, Patrocinio and another little boy together with Estolano were out in the alley back of the hotel.

There were Chinese barber shops in the basements there where Orientals were getting their heads shaved—all except the part to which their queue was appended. The boys also watched a Chinese watchmaker at work. They marveled at his long finger nails which were no less than an inch in length. A little Chinese boy happened out on the street. The other two boys dared Estolano, and he ran up and pulled the little fellow's pig tail. He howled bloody murder and a big fat Chinaman came running. But when he got to the scene of the rumpus, all three American boys had turned the corner on the way to their hotel and were nowhere to be seen.

The Larios family visited at the Lynch home. It was here at dinner that Estolano ate his first ice cream. There were three of the Lynch children, Frank, Matthias and Frederick. Frank was about Estolano's age and had a large rocking horse almost as tall as a Shetland pony. Estolano was a good horseback rider, having at that age already ridden a bucking horse and had never been thrown. Both boys got on the rocking horse at one time, Estolano in front. Somehow this rocking horse threw them both off slick and clean. Although the floor was covered with very soft carpet both got a hard fall, and it was all that Estolano could do to keep from crying. "Pleasure will bring tears," said Estolano's mother as she soothed his hurts.

While in the city the Larios family made a trip across the Bay to see the railroad train. It was something very new and the first train they had ever seen. They took a ride, and Estolano on his return to the Ranchito was simply bubbling over with excitement over the camels he had seen. "There was a band of scrawny yellow cattle along the track," he declared, "and they all had humps on their backs."

Many trips were made by the Larios family in the old time *carretas*. These two-wheeled ox-carts were made entirely of wood. Even the axles were of solid timber. The wheels were low and quite thick. It was very hard to tip them over even when hauling wood in the mountains. Tallow was used for axle grease. The screech of a *carreta* could be heard a mile or more. For a long trip there was always a top fixed over the rack which made the *carreta* look very much like an old time covered-wagon.

One time the Larios family went on a trip to the Santa Ana Ranch. There were about ten or twelve children in the party and two women. A couple of men rode on horseback and drove the two yokes of oxen pulling the screaming *carretta* packed full of sprawling youngsters. They left San Juan about nine o'clock in the morning and got to the San Benito River about lunch time. After resting for awhile under a shade tree, they proceeded the rest of the twelve-mile journey and got there just at dusk.

In the early days families used to go on washing expeditions to some river and wash great quantities of clothes. Every summer during the blackberry season the people of the Ranchito went in a *carreta* to the *Poso de Sanchez.* This was the name given to the large deep pool formed at the confluence of the Pajaro and the San Benito Rivers. During the day the women washed clothes and the men played cards. Bathing in the river was the principal diversion. Often Don Manuel would put Estolano on his back and swim across the pool with him. Two or three days would be spent at the Poso picking blackberries, feasting and camping out in the open.

Don Manuel never missed an opportunity to let Estolano go on trips with older men. José Belardez had married Juana Higuera and the family lived at the Ranchito. One day Don Manuel sent Belardez on horseback to the Santa Ana Ranch to get two fat steers. He sent Estolano along. The two horseback riders drove a yoke of oxen before them. It took them a whole day to go the twelve miles to the ranch. Early the next morning they rounded up the two steers and tied each one to an ox. It was a hot day and the four cattle, as well as the saddle horses and their riders became very thirsty. They went by way of the Hollister Ranch, as there was a deep well at that place with a windmill and a large trough full at all times with water. While the stock were drinking, Estolano went to the house to fill the canteens. Belardez and Estolano nooned under the shade of a large live oak tree for about two hours and then started on. The cattle still traveled very slowly. When the San Benito River was reached Belardez told Estolano that it would be impossible for them to get to the Ranchito that night and that they had better stay right there for the night. Estolano rode back to Hollister's Ranch and asked for some coffee and sugar. He got enough for both supper and breakfast. The lady at the ranch would take no pay for it and asked if she could help Estolano with anything else. Estolano assured her that they had plenty, as they were well supplied with *empanadas.*

Estolano and Belardez made out fine. When the morning star was half way up the zenith, Belardez who like most all early Californians could tell time at night by the stars, knew that it was time to get up. He boiled some coffee and the two had their breakfast. At noon they were back at the Ranchito.

Every year Don Manuel used to send an ox-team to the Monterey seacoast for a load of stock salt. On the Estrada ranch north of Moss Landing there were several ocean sloughs that overflowed regularly, and Estrada would gather up the salt and sell it. This coarse salt was used only for stock. Don Manuel sent Belardez with a two-yoke ox-wagon for a load of salt, and Estolano was sent with him on horseback.

Night overtook the travelers before they were across the Salinas Valley, although they had started early from home. There was no Castroville, Salinas City or Sotoville in those days. Only a few scattered ranches dotted the valley.

They passed close to the house of Don Eusebio Boronda, and he came out on horseback to see who they were. Boronda was a fine-looking old country Spaniard. He was riding a beautiful bay horse caparisoned with the most gorgeous silver-mounted saddle that Estolano had even seen. Boronda invited them to make camp at his house, but Belardez declined, saying that they would go on as far as they could while it was still light. They made camp a few miles from the Estrada Ranch and slept that night in the bed of their wagon.

In the morning just at daylight Belardez got up and started cooking breakfast.

"Estolano," he shouted suddenly, "get up quick and see the band of antelope going by." Estolano jumped up and looked. Sure enough there was a big band of antelope running by, maybe fifty or sixty head and within easy rifle shot.

Belardez laughed heartily. "Don't get excited, Estolano. Those antelope are miles away. What you are seeing is a mirage."

By the time they reached the Estrada Ranch and loaded their wagon at the salt pits, it was late afternoon. So they stayed at the ranch house that night and got an early start the next morning before daylight. At sunrise they were nearly half-way through the Salinas Valley. By noon they were at Natividad and had dinner at the Stokes Ranch. In good season that evening Belardez and Estolano were home at the Ranchito again.

The Barcelon Coyote

Chapter XIX

THE SOUVENIR

LATE ONE NIGHT just before Christmas the body of José Antonio Larios, the cousin of Don Manuel, who had come up on a visit from Mexico, was found dead about a hundred yards from the gate to the Ranchito. His throat had been cut from ear to ear.

Estolano was right on hand the next morning when Dr. MacDougall came to perform the autopsy.

"I want to see, too," insisted Estolano, as he forced his way through the crowd of grown-ups that surrounded the dining room table on which the body of the murdered man had been laid.

"All right, Estolano," said the tall Scotch doctor good-naturedly. "You and I will make the examination together."

The doctor had turned the body over on its side in order to examine the knife wounds in the back.

"Look, Estolano. Do you see those openings? They are wounds made with a knife." He drew open the gashes. As he did so, Estolano could see a bulging layer of fat, like he had often seen when a hog was being butchered at the Ranchito.

"Just like a stuck hog," observed Estolano.

"You are very observing," commented the doctor tersely.

Dr. MacDougall then rolled the body over on its back. Together he and Estolano examined the slash across the throat.

The doctor with his fingers opened the cut.

"You see here, Estolano, the knife severed not only the windpipe but the two jugular veins as well."

Estolano looked very carefully into the wound as Dr. MacDougall pointed out these parts of the throat.

"Now, Estolano, we must make a report. Shall we say that the murdered man met his death at the hands of someone armed with a sharp knife?"

"It looks to me like my cousin was killed twice. There must have been two murderers. One killed Cousin Tony by cutting his throat and the other by stabbing him in the back."

Dr. MacDougall looked at Estolano in surprise. "You are a regular little lawyer," he declared in admiration.

Don Manuel's Yaqui swine herd, Miguel, and another Indian who helped him with the hogs had been seen in San Juan the night of the murder. Miguel lived about two or three miles west of the Ranchito house up near the crest of the mountains where Don Manuel had built a cabin for him and his family.

The next morning after the murder the officers called at Miguel's house. Miguel and the other Indian were out at the time herding the hogs. The officers searched the house and under Miguel's bed found a bloody knife. It was a one blade jack knife with a spring in the back to open it and hold the blade firm. Taking this with them as evidence they went out and arrested the two Indians.

There used to be a large livery stable on Third Street opposite the Sebastopol Hotel. The doors of this barn were large and wide. A person going along the street could look right into the barn. There were large rings fastened in the ceiling to which horses were tied when they were being curried or harnessed.

The crowd of townspeople with their two Indian prisoners did not bother to take them clear on down to the Alameda where the third tree from the right generally served as the town gallows. Instead when the crowd of men and boys came shuffling past the livery barn they stopped. The two Indians were tied by their necks from the iron rings in the ceiling. Their feet were about a foot off the floor. Estolano who seldom missed anything going on in San Juan squeezed himself in and watched the Indians as they slowly strangled to death.

Juan Hidalgo was an insane man who lived for several years at the Ranchito. He was a Chilian. He had been the ranch cook at the Santa Ana when Frank Lynch from San Francisco had the ranch rented. When Lynch gave up the lease he made Don Manuel a present of this Chilian. Hidalgo was a good cook. At the Ranchito he baked the bread, roasted the meat and made the Chili sauce. Estolano and the rest of the children thought it great fun to torment this unbalanced little man. He would sometimes chase them but could never run fast enough to catch them. Often when Estolano would be going past Hidalgo's room he would see the lonely fellow talking with the mice in the cupboard. He seemed to think that he knew them and that they were the only friends he had in the world.

Estolano and an albino boy named Narcisso German one afternoon were sitting on the fence watching Lupe Larios' husband, Luciano Salas, taking the rack off of the ox wagon. This was a large four-wheeled American wagon with iron tires on the wheels. Salas had the Chilian cook out helping him. The two men were lifting together on the rack. Salas was a very powerful man and he became very impatient when the Chilian failed to lift his share.

"Lift!" shouted Salas.

The cook paid no attention, and Salas slapped him.

Instantly Hidalgo pulled out a knife about a foot long and ran it the whole length into Salas' stomach. The weapon was so crude that the Chilian was unable to pull the blade out of the victim.

Estolano jumped down from the fence and ran to the aid of

Salas. A torrent of blood spurted out as Estolano twisted the blade and removed it from the body of the staggering man. "This crazy Chilian has killed me!" were Salas' last words as he toppled over.

Don Manuel, hearing of the tragedy, came rushing out of the house armed with his old army lance, the weapon of his youthful days. With lance uplifted the heavy set old man started in pursuit of Hidalgo. The cook, however, ran down through the orchard to the willows and escaped along the Monterey road.

Estolano had watched the direction taken by the fleeing cook, and when the officers from San Juan arrived he told them which way to go. He ran along with them. The posse soon overtook the crazy man. When ordered to throw up his hands Hidalgo raised only one hand. The officers ordered, "Put up your other hand!" The tantalizing Chilian promptly lowered his first hand and raised the other one. "No. That won't do," shouted the officers. Hidalgo finally put up both hands. He was taken to Monterey where he was tried, found insane and sent to the Stockton Asylum.

Estolano, one morning on his way to school, met along the fence just beyond the cemetery a big-faced, rather half-witted Indian boy that he had often beaten playing marbles. Later, on his arrival at school, Estolano learned that a sheep herder had been murdered in the Alameda the night before. When the body was found early in the morning it was clad only in an undershirt. It was a cold morning and the body was covered with white frost.

Estolano told the posse that was quickly formed that he had seen this Indian boy prowling along the road past the Ranchito. When the posse caught up with the Indian they found him wearing the shirt and pants missing from the body of the dead sheep herder!

A rope an inch or so thick and maybe sixty feet long was

secured and the Indian boy taken down to the overhanging limb of the third tree on the Alameda. The mob didn't bother even to tie the boy's hands. The rope was thrown over the limb and everybody that could get hold yanked on the rope. The Indian was pulled up in the air so fast that he was still conscious when his body struck the limb of the tree. Instantly the boy threw his arms around the limb and clung to the lower side.

Several men got hold of his feet and pulled him down. This time they tied his hands and then pulled him up again. When he ceased to struggle the end of the rope was tied around another tree and the body left dangling there for the rest of the day.

After school Estolano and several other school boys came down to see. They pulled up and down on the rope and made the hands and feet of the swollen-faced corpse jiggle around like a jumping jack.

"I'm going to take home a souvenir," declared Estolano. He reached up and pulled off one of the Indian's boots.

At the Ranchito Estolano was proudly showing his souvenir when Don Manuel himself came into the *sala*.

"Estolano, you get that thing right out of this house. You take it over to the cemetery and you leave it there!"

"I can't never have nothing," lamented Estolano as he reluctantly set out for the cemetery with the dead Indian's boot.

Aunt Pilar,
Famous San Juan
Midwife

and Her Grave
on the Hill

Chapter XX

ESTOLANO HAD A COW OF HIS OWN

ONLY A SMALL NUMBER of cattle were kept at the Ranchito, just a few milch cows and some stock to butcher for meat. The Larios cattle, numbering several thousand head, were kept in winter at the Santa Ana Ranch. In the summer-time they were taken up in the mountains to the Panoche Valley and the Vallecitos (Little Valleys). The Panoche was then all open country.

The vaqueros all lived at the Ranchito. There were Manuelito and Dolores Larios, and of the Higuera family, Antonio, José and Frank. José Espinoza was a Santa Barbara cowboy who worked at the Ranchito for several years. Francisco and Dolores Arroyo from the San Joaquin Ranch were at the San Antonio for quite awhile. Alifonso Ramirez, a fine looking Mexican, also worked for Don Manuel handling cattle.

A big band of saddle horses ranged the hills of the Ranchito, fifty or sixty head. The *"Caponera,"* as the bell mare was called, led the band. All the other horses knew the sound of the bell she wore around her neck and would follow her. When the cowboys wanted a saddle horse they would whistle. The bell mare would come right up into the corral, the rest of the horses following her.

There were always a few colts in the band of saddle horses. One stallion ran loose with the band. He was a very beautiful horse that had been captured wild over in the San Joaquin Valley. He was a pinto, spotted pinkish-red and dappled about the shoulders and rump.

Whenever there was a nice two-year-old colt in the *manada*, some one of the boys at the Ranchito always wanted it.

"All right," Don Manuel would say, "but remember, your saddle must go on before your brand." That meant that the boy must break the colt to ride before he could claim it as his own.

When Estolano was to be given a colt, his saddle would be placed on the astonished animal and the colt led down to the cornfield where the ground was plowed. It was nice and soft in case of a fall. A long rope would be attached to the colt's hackamore, which is the rawhide muzzle around a horse's mouth always used by bronco busters. The colt was blindfolded and Don Manuel would lift Estolano up in the saddle. The instant the blind was removed the colt would start on a run, bucking his best. Don Manuel, mounted on a good horse, would always ride along side of his son. Estolano could usually stay on a calf's back, which is a whole lot harder than keeping one's seat on a horse. However, Estolano would sometimes start leaving the saddle very unceremoniously. Don Manuel would seize him by the arm and set him back into the saddle. In this way the colt would be ridden until it gave up, and then was Estolano's own.

The same colt was seldom ridden more than once to claim ownership. The boys earned them with their first ride. An expert at reining a horse was employed on the Ranchito, and he broke all the colts to the bit afterwards and finished training them.

Each Larios boy had his own brand. Don Manuel's own was the letter "L." Each boy's brand was an "L" but with a different ending. Gracia's brand was an "L" with a half moon at each end. Dolores' brand had the letter "O" at the ends. Patrocinio's had an "L" with a "P" on the under side. Estolano's was an "L" with an "S" in the center. Estolano already had his brand on three horses before he was ten years old.

"Pisa Flores" was the name of Estolano's own cow. Along with Estolano's three colts and his sheep, Pisa Flores wore Estolano's own brand. This pet, when Estolano called, would come to him and let him milk her right into his mouth. Her name, "Pisa Flores" meant "Walking on Flowers."

A rodeo or round-up was usually held each spring and fall in the vicinity of San Juan. These were for the purpose of returning all stray cattle to the ranches to which they belonged. A central location would be selected and on the appointed day each rancher and his string of cowboys would drive all the stray cattle from his home ranch to the rodeo ground. A circle of cowboys would be formed around the milling cattle as they arrived and generally by noon, if all the ranchers were on hand, the work of parting out the cattle would commence.

Around the larger ring several smaller rings of cowboys would first be formed representing the various ranches taking part in the rodeo. Each ranch owner would have his own expert "parter." These selected cowboys knew perfectly the earmark and brand of their respective ranches and could handle their horses well. When all was ready these "parters" would ride into the bunch of cattle and begin cutting out those belonging to each individual ranch. These would be driven out of the circle and turned over to the cowboys of the ranch to which the animal belonged. This parting would continue until all the stray cattle had been worked over.

Sometimes a steer would bolt out of the circle, and then the fun would begin. Usually one cowboy alone would take after the steer and, catching him by the tail, turn him over. When the steer would regain its feet, it would find itself headed in the direction of the circle that it had just broken out of, and would be easily driven back. But sometimes a steer had to be roped in order to turn it back and this required two cowboys.

Estolano attended the rodeos quite often. He always rode a good horse and thought himself quite a cowboy. On one occasion when the rodeo was taking place on the Dan Murphy ranch north of Gilroy, a steer broke out of the circle close to where Estolano was on guard, and he naturally took after it to bring it back. Don Manuel saw what was happening and immediately dispatched two cowboys to the scene, one to take care of the steer and the other to look after Estolano. The rodeo ground was full of squirrel holes and Don Manuel was afraid that Estolano's horse might stumble and break Estolano's neck. The two cowboys succeeded in their mission and both Estolano and the run-away steer were brought back to their respective places to the great humiliation of Estolano.

When the stray cattle were all parted out, each rancher, together with his own band of cowboys, would set out for their particular ranch, driving their stray cattle before them. Calves followed their mothers and were always marked and branded at the home ranch before being turned out on the range again.

Round-ups for horses were a different matter. A large corral on some ranch was used in which to corral the horses. In here they were lassoed and branded.

A band of wild horses were crowding out of the gate of a corral in the Santa Ana Valley. José Espinoza, Don Manuel's cowboy from Santa Barbara, was crouching beside the gate post. He was wearing his quirt on his wrist and his spurs on his boots. Suddenly, as a dark bay horse was squeezing out of the corral, he sprang upon its back. There was no bridle or rope on the horse and of course no saddle. The startled horse bolted straight forward. Bucking was no name for its actions. But Jose stayed on its back. With one hand he held to the horse's mane and with his right hand lashed the terrified animal with his quirt. Two horsemen followed. The horse, tired after a mile or so of hard running and bucking, gave up and slowed down.

This gave José a chance to jump off, and he rode back to the corral with one of the men. José had been with the Larios outfit for two or three years and was well liked. Don Manuel, in recognition of his prowess in riding so fearlessly, made José a present of the horse.

"Oh, if I could only ride like José!" meditated Estolano as he sat his horse and looked on.

Remijio Capitán of the Paradon Rancheria

Chapter XXI

THE LONG WALK

"No sir!" declared Estolano emphatically. "They aren't going to play any trick like that on me." Estolano and his nephew, Bernardo, were lugging Estolano's saddle and bridle out to the horse corral where Tom, an old saddle horse, was dozing in the sun. "My folks can't skip out and leave me home like this."

Estolano's father and mother had gone on a visit in the family carriage to Estolano's sister, Alta Graciá Barcelon, who lived at the Cantua about eighteen miles from San Juan. This was the first time his parents had ever left Estolano behind when going on a visit any place. He resented their action and was determined to follow them.

Tom was a saddle horse so old that he had been pensioned off as having served his time. But although he was a little stiff in the front legs the boys thought that he could carry the two of them the eighteen miles if they traveled slow. They put Estolano's saddle on his back and then got an old saddle blanket for Bernardo to sit on and ride behind. Sneaking out the back way from the ranch, they struck out for San Juan. When they came to Adolphe Vache's store at the corner of Third and Washington Street, they tied old Tom to the hitching rack and went in to buy some lunch for the trip.

Bernardo and Estolano hadn't gotten away from the Ranchito as secretly as they had thought. Estolano had been left in charge of his two sisters, Lupe and Juana, who with their families were living at the time at the Ranchito. Juana caught sight of the two boys on old Tom's back and had immediately surmised that they might be setting out for the Cantua.

"José," said Juana to her husband, "I just saw the two boys leaving the ranch. You better catch up with them and see what they are up to."

José got on a saddle horse and slowly followed at a distance behind the fugitives, hoping to give them a little leeway before he turned them back. At Vache's he watched the boys tie old Tom up to the hitching rail and then go inside the store. José quietly untied old Tom and led him back to the Ranchito. He knew that the boys would soon come trudging home. He had no intention of punishing them, simply wanting to outsmart them. Nothing would be said, and the boys would be given to think that no one even suspected that they had started to run away.

Inside the tiny store Estolano and Bernardo were busy buying what they thought in their childish minds would make a splendid lunch. They purchased fifty cents worth of candy, a few Jenny Lind cookies and a bottle of apple cider. To their consternation when they came out of the store their saddle horse had disappeared!

"I just know Juana did that!" declared Estolano. "Stole our horse!"

"Oh, well," declared Bernardo. "We've got a nice lunch. We can go and have a picnic somewhere. Play we are on our way to the Cantua."

"No," declared Estolano, stubbornly. "They aren't going to stop people like us." After a pause he announced: "We'll walk to the Cantua!"

It was ten o'clock of a hot summer day when the boys left San Juan. After two hours of walking they were still in the "Lane," the five mile stretch of road leading out of town. It was tremendously warm and both were nearly dead with thirst and hunger. They sat down by a fence and munched on their cookies and candy. They finished up the rest of their cider. When they were through they were still as thirsty and hungry as before. But they resolutely continued their march.

They foolishly thought to find water in the San Benito River. But they did not know that this stretch of the river is usually dry in summer. When they reached the river bed and looked around they were bitterly disappointed. There wasn't a drop of water in sight anywhere.

They rested in the shade of a tree for quite a while pondering what they should do. Both agreed that it would be almost as hard to get back as it would be to go on forward.Finally they got to their feet and went on their way again. About two or three miles beyond the river they saw two men on horseback riding towards them. When they met Estolano recognized one as Miguel Castro, the oldest of the Mariano Castro family. He had married a cousin of Estolano, Josefa, a daughter of Aunt Pilar. Castro had a canteen hanging on the horn of his saddle. As Estolano knew him well, he had no hesitancy in asking for a drink of water.

"Certainly," said Castro. Unfastening the canteen he handed it to the boys, all the while a big smile spreading over his swarthy face. Two or three big gulps went down Estolano's throat before he realized that it wasn't water that he was drinking.

"That's whisky!" choked Estolano as he looked up in disgust at the old man.

Bernardo, who had also taken a swig, confirmed Estolano's declaration. The old Californian only laughed at the joke he thought he had played on the desperately thirsty boys. "But it's more than whisky you boys will be needing if you make it to Barcelon's house before night!" Castro offered the boys more.

But they declined, thirsty as they were, thanking him just the same.

Again they were on their way. The liquor certainly stimulated them for the time being. Almost immediately they began amusing themselves by picking up stones and throwing them viciously at the little birds called *Tapa camino,* or road stoppers, that were numerous along the road.

It was dusk when they reached the road house kept by a Frenchman named Avy. This sheepman had rented the Tres Pinos Ranch from Estolano's brother, Antonio Larios, who had lived there for a short time after his marriage but who now lived in San Juan. Avy had built a little lumber shack along side of the road and sold meals and liquor. The boys had spent every cent they had in San Juan and so had no money to buy anything with. "We'll stop in just for a drink of water," confided Estolano to Bernardo. "They won't charge us anything for that."

Estolano was soon telling Avy the bland story of how someone had stolen their horse, and they were having to go on foot to the Cantua to find his parents. Avy's wife who had been listening was moved to pity. Going into the kitchen, she returned bringing each of the little tramps a nice large sandwich of bread and meat and a piece of apple pie.

The wagon road the next mile or so from the Avy road house followed the river bed. Here the water in the San Benito River varied from ten to twenty feet in width and was from ankle to knee deep. The road wove in and out of the water and the boys had to wade through it pretty often. But it was summer and the evening was still warm, so they did not mind getting their feet wet.

Where the road finally left the river bed there was a little hill and a large patch of willows. It was now quite dark. The boys were getting a little nervous. They just knew there were bears in the woods. Suddenly as they began to climb the hill they heard right along side of the road a bear give a startled grunt. They were scared half to death. And did they run! The perpetrator of their fright, however, they soon discovered was not a bear but was one of three big hogs. An old sow, getting scared, had aroused her sleepy companions, and together they were all scampering away in the darkness.

About a mile farther on the boys turned off from the main road and went through a gate. A wagon trail led up to Barcelon's house where Estolano's parents were supposed to be. Trudging along this trail half a mile farther, they came to the house. Everything was dark. Estolano went up to the front door and knocked good and hard.

"Who's there?" asked someone inside. Estolano recognized the voice of his sister, Alta Gracia. He answered loudly: "Estolano Larios."

Estolano's mother rushed to the door at once. Not only was she surprised but she was badly scared, thinking that something dreadful had happened at the Ranchito and that Estolano had been sent to notify them.

"You rode all this way—"

"We walked!" broke in Bernardo as he slumped into a chair.

"Well you children must be nearly starved."

"No," declared Estolano. "We ate at Avy's in Tres Pinos."

Beds were made up on the floor and the two boys were almost immediately sound asleep. Everybody had had their breakfast the next morning before they even woke up. It was almost impossible for either of the two boys to get out of bed their muscles were so sore. Every move almost brought a scream. Estolano's mother was all for settling with the two boys with a good rawhide quirt for running away from home. But Don Manuel interfered.

"I'll guarantee they will never run away from home again," the jolly old Don declared, his tummy shaking with laughter, as the two boys tried painfully to walk about the room.

"The boys have whipped themselves," he laughed.

Don Manuel Larios, 1852

Chapter XXII

ESTOLANO BECOMES A
SOLDIER

ESTOLANO AND HIS MOTHER were on their way one Sunday morning as usual to attend Mass at the Mission Church. As they approached the National Hotel they were surprised to see a great many men congregated there all dressed in blue uniforms. As they passed the swinging doors leading into the hotel Estolano pushed them open and peeked inside. To his surprise the hotel was simply full of men in blue.

San Juan was a Rebel Town during the Civil War and things had become so bad that the Government found it necessary to send a company of infantrymen and a troop of cavalry to San Juan to maintain order.

Numerous Southerners who had flocked into San Juan after the American Occupation of California were now bent on taking California out of the Union and into the ranks of the Confederacy. Their boast had been that the flag of the United States could not fly in San Juan. With the coming of the Federal troops, the American flag was promptly hoisted to the top of the flagpole on the Plaza. Once again it floated majestically over San Juan. The hostile Southern element could do nothing but look on in chagrin.

The army officers established themselves and their wives at the Plaza Hotel, while the enlisted men were quartered in the National Hotel about a block away and in tents pitched north of the Mission buildings. Rooms were also rented in the Mission Corridors for the guard house, the tailor shops and for storing medical supplies. The Plaza Hotel became the center of social gaiety in San Juan.

Dress parades were held daily. The infantry used the Plaza for its parade ground, while the cavalry went through their maneuvers down on the flat to the north of the Mission orchard. Hundreds of people, especially on Sundays, would line the hillside north of the Mission and watch the evolutions of the cavalry on the field below. To the people of San Juan who were naturally given to horsemanship, it was a thrilling spectacle to see the cavalrymen put spurs to their horses and charge across the field, all the while brandishing their sabres and executing "Right Cut!" "Left Cut!" "Upper Cut!"

Dress parades of the infantry on the Plaza also called forth the admiration of the native Californians. Where once a half dozen Spanish soldiers had stood guard over the Mission and the Mission Fathers, there was now a full company of well-drilled American soldiers wheeling and turning and presenting "Company Front!"

Four army tailors had their shop in the Mission corridors. They were all Frenchmen and Estolano knew them well. These tailors used to walk up to the Ranchito to get fresh milk to drink. The head tailor was especially fond of Estolano and made him a little uniform out of the discarded suits of the soldiers.

It was not long before the little Spanish boys of San Juan had a military company of their own. Santana Butron was the captain. He was fifteen years old. Flaviano German and Estolano were among the members of the company. All were armed with wooden sabres which they flourished in true military fashion at the command of their captain. When the company had become quite proficient Major Cremony, who was the commanding officer of Camp Low, the military post in San

Juan, ordered Captain Butron and his company to give an exhibition drill on the Plaza in front of the Plaza Hotel. Major Cremony and his staff looked on from the balcony of the hotel. A big crowd of San Juan people were assembled on the Plaza to watch the boys. Captain Butron and his company conducted themselves with such distinction that at the completion of their drill the crowd broke out in cheers and Major Cremony, coming down, pinned a big military brass-eagle on Captain Butron's breast.

Many native Californians enlisted while the troops were in San Juan. Among them were Estolano's half brother, José Jésus Higuera, and Estolano's nephew, Frank Rojas. A very pretty Spanish girl married the trumpeter, Miranda, of the cavalry troop. When later the soldiers got orders to leave San Juan and go to fight Indians in Arizona Territory, this girl lost all her courage. She finally refused to go with her trumpeter husband and he had to leave her behind. With the departure of the two hundred troops all the gaiety of San Juan seemed to have gone with them. The few months the troops were in San Juan had given the historic old town a touch of glamor that it had not known since the time of General Castro twenty years before.

Dona Maria del Rosario Armas de Larios, 1857

Chapter XXIII

THE
MAKING OF A BULLFIGHTER

ESTOLANO, now ten years old, was fast becoming a very promising bullfighter. A good matador has to be not only brave, almost to the point of fool-hardiness, but he has to be very agile and quick witted as well. A thick-witted fellow stands no chance whatever in a bull ring when pitted against a powerful, ferocious bull. Estolano was nimble and quick-witted and, what was still more important, he was bold.

Around San Juan there were quite a number of good bullfighters for him to pattern after. Claro Echeverria, who lived up around Los Picachos near the Santa Ana Ranch was one of the best. Another great bullfighter was Benigno Soto who lived up in the Tranquillon. But the greatest bullfighter and bull rider of them all was Estolano's own cousin, Ramon, now a young man, the son of Aunt Pilar.

For the bullfights at the Ranchito Estolano's mother had humored him by making him a special pair of *pantalonas.* These are pants with wide bottoms and open along the leg as far up as the knee. The sides of Estolano's *pantalonas* she had ornamented with a strip of narrow black braid on which she sewed rows of silver buttons from top to bottom. For a shirt Estolano had persuaded her to go to the store and buy some cloth from the same bolt that Adelia Saunder's mother had used recently to make a dress for her little daughter. Adelia was Estolano's sweetheart, and he wanted a shirt made from the same material as her dress. Around Estolano's waist was tied a bright red sash. On the side of his black stiff-rimmed hat he wore a small bunch of chicken feathers, black, red and white, tied together in a cockade. Secretly Estolano felt quite proud of himself.

Don Manuel never let Santa Ana's Day go by without a grand celebration. Bull fighting, dancing and feasting at the Ranchito lasted never less than three days. Invitations to the fiesta were sent out weeks ahead to all friends and relatives as far away as Monterey, Santa Cruz and Pescadero. All San Juan was invited en masse. At the appointed time people flocked to the Ranchito by the hundreds, all eager to help Don Manuel celebrate his patron saint's day in a fitting manner.

Preparations for the fiesta were begun sometimes a month in advance. First of all the bull ring, always called the Plaza, had to be built. This Plaza, about eighty feet wide and a hundred feet long from north to south, was located on the south side of the Ranchito house. The construction of the stockade was in the hands of Don Manuel's Indians, who from many such repetitions were experts at the task. Post holes were dug in the ground some ten feet apart and about two and a half feet deep. Two posts ten feet long were then set solidly in each of the holes. In between the two posts room was left wide enough for long poles to be laid in between them. These horizontal poles were fastened securely by rawhide thongs to each other and to the posts. In this way a fence was constructed about eight feet high and much too strong for a bull to break down. There were no gates. Simply the bars were taken down wherever an entrance was desired. Each year the bull ring was built anew. When a celebration was over, Don Manuel's Indians would take down the fence and store it away for the next year.

Next came the building of a series of brush houses or *enramadas* along the back of the Ranchito house itself. A few simple arbors were also built in the front yard or Patio. These were made of willow boughs principally. Each *enramada* was equipped with an outdoor fireplace or Hornilla. A cook was assigned to each *enramada.* A long table with benches was provided on which to sit and eat. All visitors at the fiesta were given free food during the three days of the celebration. Everyone was welcome to go in at any time of the day or night to one of these eating places and be served with beans, Chili sauce, tortillas and *empanadas,* or meat pies.

The fiercest bulls in the early days were those roaming on the east side of Gavilan Peak. Out on this range the bulls saw no one for long stretches of time, and when they were lassooed and brought to the Ranchito the sight of a person on foot made them almost frantic.

Several days before the celebration Don Manuel would send out six or eight vaqueros to the Gavilan to capture the wildest bulls to be found. The cowboys worked in pairs. Each set had two yokes of tame oxen with them. As fast as a wild bull was lassoed it would be tied securely by the horns to those of an ox. When enough bulls had been captured the expedition would set out on its return to the Ranchito, each tame ox tugging a wild bull along as a prisoner at its side. At the Ranchito the wild bulls, each still tied to its tame companion, were kept in a little pasture adjoining the bull ring.

Visitors and relatives simply swarmed about the Ranchito the three days of the fiesta. The men rode their finest horses. Some used the old-style Spanish saddles. These were very elaborate and cost hundreds of dollars. Spanish saddles themselves were merely a framework, like a pack saddle. They had a horn, cantle, cinch and stirrups. But over this framework was placed the *"mochilla."* This was the pride of the old Californians' hearts. It was a leather covering that fitted over the saddle frame and went well down over the horse as far as the stirrups themselves. It was the elaborate embroidering of the *mochilla* that made it so attractive in the eyes of the Californians. Don Manuel once caught old John Gilroy hard up for money and succeeded in buying a *mochilla* from the old Scot for a mere five hundred dollars.

Others of the visitors rode the newer style Mexican saddles. These were leather covered and were made much the same as present-day saddles. Their elegance consisted in their silver mountings. Every part of the saddle that could be decorated was covered with silver trimmings. The cantle or back of the saddle was silver mounted. Oftentimes the owner's name was engraved on a special silver plate.

Many of the young women who attended the fiesta also came on horseback. All had silver mounted bridles and martingales. Their side saddles rested on silver-embroidered *"caronas."* These were elaborate blankets and were placed over the saddle blankets before the saddle was put on. The young ladies themselves wore rich riding habits. Their half high stove pipe hats were decorated with a black plume. The skirts of their riding habits reached a foot or more below their stirrups. And these girls were good riders, too. Often they would give chase along with the men and help "tail" the bull when it was turned out of the Plaza.

During the bullfights as many as two hundred women and children would be seated upstairs in the balcony overlooking the bull ring. Below, sitting on the fence surrounding the Plaza were as many men and boys as could climb on. The hillside to the south of the house was a natural grandstand. Around the outside of the fence and on the hillside at least two hundred men on horseback sat their horses during the bullfights and watched the spectacle.

The bullfights began about one o'clock in the afternoon, shortly after lunch and lasted three or four hours each day. A wild bull tied to its companion ox, would be driven into the Plaza. Once inside, it was held securely with lariats until the rawhide thong fastening it to the tame ox was removed. The ox was then driven from the arena. The bull now found itself alone in an enclosure it could neither scale nor break through.

While the bull stared angrily about the Plaza, several bullfighters on horseback would ride into the enclosure. At the same time those who were going to fight this particular bull on foot would climb down off the fence. Each bullfighter was given his turn at fighting the bull.

A matador or bullfighter on foot, holding a red blanket in front of him advances across the Plaza in the direction of the bull. The waving blanket sets the bull wild. It lowers its head and rushes towards its victim. As the bull nears the matador the latter steps aside and now holds the blanket to one side at arm's length instead of in front of him. The bull continues its charge, not being clever enough to realize that the matador is no longer behind the waving cloth. Just as the bull is about to crash through the blanket the matador jerks it away, making sport of the bull as it goes lumbering past.

As soon as the bull gets its huge body stopped and turns itself around to see what has become of its tormentor, he finds the matador with the red cloth again facing him. The bull lowers its head once more and charges. Again the bull is fooled. The nimble matador simply sidesteps the bull's oncoming rush. After four or five rounds of this sort the first matador leaves the Plaza and another matador takes his place. The bull is given no rest. After several matadors have taken turns tormenting the bull, the horsemen take up the fight.

Bullfighting on horseback requires a well trained horse as well as an expert rider. The horse and the bull are kept facing one another. The horse is never allowed to stand sideways to the bull. As the bull and rider face one another the bull fighter waves his red cloth. This is usually his lady love's red shawl if he has been able to persuade her to lend it to him for the occasion. The bridle reins are always held in the rider's left hand.

As the bull lowers its head to charge the rider clucks to the horse and pulls to the left. The horse springs past on the bull's right side. After the bull and the horse have passed one another, the horse with its rider turns about and again faces the bull. Again the bullfighter waves the red cloth. The bull bellows, swings its tail and decides to make still another charge. He lowers his head and dashes towards the horse and rider. Again the horse is too nimble. The bull finds the horse is gone and the perplexed animal sometimes almost crashes into the fence itself.

When the bull is tired out and will no longer fight, just simply shakes its head when the blanket is dragged across its horns, the fight is over for that bull. A gate is opened and the bull driven ignominiously out of the arena. Then comes the fun for the horsemen outside. "Tailing the bull" is great sport. The bull is made to turn a somersault as it lopes away to freedom. Several horsemen race after the fleeing bull. The leader seizes the bull by the tail and with a lift of the animal and a twist of the tail over the rider's leg he sends the bull rolling head over heels. If the first rider fails, the second seizes the tail and over the bull rolls. Should the bull reach a certain point in the hills before anyone was able to tail it the bull won, and the chase was given up.

About four o'clock each afternoon, after the bullfighting was over for the day, the hordes of visitors would all go down to the two big willow trees which used to stand about five hundred feet from the house on the other side of the *Arroyito*. There they were greeted with a barbecue feast consisting of beef, mutton, tortillas and all the Chili sauce one wanted. Wine was served freely to all.

After the barbecue all would go to the main hall or *sala* of the house and dance throughout the night and all the next day until the bullfighting began again. Along the walls of the *sala* there were nice benches. The women sat on one side of the room while the men sat on the other. The music never stopped. The orchestra consisted generally of a first and second violin, a Spanish guitar, a base guitar and a flute. All the old Spanish dances were played: Jotas, Jarabes, Sones and Fandangoes. The modern dances were the contra danza, on the order of lancers, the waltz, schottische, mazurka, varsovianna and polka. All these, the old and the new, were danced by Don Manuel's carefree friends and relatives.

Among the Californians a fiesta wasn't a fiesta without gambling. Monte was the master game. At the Santa Ana celebrations one entire *enramada* was set apart for the Monte dealer. Everyone who could squeeze around the table did so. An Irishman used to deal monte at all the fiestas in San Juan. He went by the nickname of "Pongle, Don." He would deal out the two cards and then begin crying: "Pongle, Don! Pongle, Don!" This was about all the Spanish he knew. It meant for everyone to come up and place their money on the card of their choice.

Everything was free at the Santa Ana celebrations, even wine and grape brandy. But Heaven help the man who got drunk or boisterous. There was always a committee consisting of five or six trustworthy men selected by Don Manuel who kept order during the celebration. Cases of drunkenness were rare, but on one occasion one afternoon a man who was a great hand for hard liquor was carried down from the dance hall by the committee to the creek and then after a thorough dousing led back to the house, where he was locked up in a room with a bed in it on which he could sleep off his over-indulgence.

Bull riding was another sport hugely enjoyed at the Santa Ana celebrations. A man trying to ride a perfectly wild bull furnishes no end of entertainment to a crowd. The bull will jump and buck and do just about everything to unseat its rider. To make these wild bulls buck even harder firecrackers were often used to frighten the animal still more.

Not satisfied with riding a bull face forward, Ramon, Estolano's cousin, would ride them facing backward. He had been riding bulls each day at the Ranchito celebration face forward with never a spill. On one particular day he was billed to ride a big red bull, tormented with exploding firecrackers, and face backwards! This was to be the supreme test of Ramon's bull-riding ability. The bull was thrown and the firecrackers tied to its horns, feet and tail. Then Ramon jumped on the bull's back, face backwards, the firecrackers were lighted and the bull let up. The firecrackers began exploding. All pandemonium broke loose. The bull snorted, jumped and then started racing. Of all the bucking and roaring and hooting, cheering and hollering! But amid it all Ramon kept his seat and came out victorious, riding the bull until it gave up exhausted.

Don Manuel's favorite saddle horse, Regalo, was so well trained that he could be turned loose in the Plaza and would fight a bull all by himself. Regalo of his own accord would face the bull. Then when the bull would charge Regalo would jump aside and let the bull rush past. For four or five rounds he would evade the bull. Then when the gate was opened he would trot out of the arena amid the loud applause of the multitude.

The only bull ever killed in the Plaza at the Ranchito was a spotted black and white beast with long sharp horns. The bull had hardly been turned into the Plaza when Amadeo, a middle-aged half tipsy Indian began climbing over the fence.

"I can fight a bull just as good as other people can," was his drunken boast.

Amadeo's wife with a baby in her arms was begging him to stay out. She was tugging at his clothes trying to hold him back. But Amadeo was just tipsy enough to pull away from his wife and flounder into the ring. Before he realized what was happening he found himself standing all alone facing an oncoming bull. Amadeo, in trying to run away, stumbled and fell flat on his stomach. The bull drove one of its horns under the

Indian's belt and then with a long sweep of its head tossed poor Amadeo high over the fence.

With the Indian out of the way bullfighters on horseback now began fighting the bull in earnest. It came the turn for a young man nicknamed "Dummy" to enter. He was a very young bullfighter, about twenty or so, and was riding a beautiful red bay horse not yet well broken to the Spanish bit. The fight had only begun when his horse, though active, failed to respond to the bit quick enough. The bull drove one horn straight into the center of its body and the horse's entrails poured right out on the ground.

The crowd now began clamoring for the life of the bull. Everywhere people were shouting:

"He killed a horse!"

"He half killed an Indian!"

"That bull is too dangerous to be allowed at large on the range!"

Don Manuel finally gave his consent to have it killed, and he furnished his army sword. Claro Echeverria was chosen to do the killing.

Claro borrowed Don Manuel's fighting horse, Regalo, and gave the people a very thrilling exhibition of bull fighting. Claro faced Regalo to the bull. As the bull with its head lowered to strike came charging, Regalo jumped aside, letting the bull go by. At the third pass Claro reined Regalo towards the side of the bull, and, as it charged, he drove Don Manuel's sword home its full length between the bull's shoulders. The sword pierced the bull's heart, and it dropped dead in its tracks.

Between acts during these Santa Ana bullfights, while the horsemen were tailing a fleeing bull and the vaqueros were bringing in a new bull tied to an ox for the next bullfight, the boys of the Ranchito would often be allowed to drive in one of their fighting calves and give an exhibition. These youngsters would show off the same as the men. Some were on foot and some were on "horseback." Their horses, however, were generally willow switches, often carved in such a way as to make them look like pinto horses. All the boys had nice ropes. The reins of their stick horses they usually decorated with bright metal clasps taken from old hoop skirts such as the women wore at that time.

There was a red bull calf that was exceedingly savage. One afternoon it was brought in. Before it was turned loose Estolano approached the balcony where the women and girls were looking down.

"Adelia," he called, "won't you loan me your red shawl? I want it to fight this calf with."

Estolano was on his stick horse. Adelia looked down from the edge of the balcony. It was a severe test for the little girl's love. She was just a little bit unwilling to let Estolano have her nice red shawl to get all dirty and torn.

While Estolano was standing there waiting for Adelia's decision the other boys, without his knowing it, purposely turned the calf loose. Instantly the little bull made a dash for the red sash Estolano was wearing. Bunting Estolano terrifically in the back it sent him sprawling flat on his face in the manure and dirt of the arena.

Estolano felt pretty cheap and abashed as he got up amid all the hooting, laughing and hollering. Undaunted, however, he walked out of the ring, went into the house and changed his clothes. Then going up on the balcony he won the coveted shawl from Adelia. Back into the ring he went. He simply wore the calf out. He fought it to a finish.

Amid the rousing cheers of the spectators Estolano stalked out of the arena. Everybody was admiring not only his ability as a bullfighter, but his pluck in returning to the fight.

"Just like his old father," some were saying.

"He'll make a real bullfighter when he gets a little older."

Walking in triumph out on the balcony he came and sat

down for a moment beside Adelia.

"Where is my shawl?" she asked petulantly—her only greeting. "Did you get it torn?"

Without answering, the crestfallen Estolano made his way back down stairs and out in the arena with the other boys. As the perplexed young lover strolled over to the adobe wall of the house he pondered silently on the selfishness of girls.

"My fighting a bull to the finish," he thought to himself, "is nothing to her! All *she* worries about is her old shawl."

Frederick A. MacDougall, M.D.
(From the photograph of a painting)

Chapter XXIV

THE PROBLEM CHILD

IT WAS ALREADY almost dark. The three boys were beginning
to fight. Estolano and his nephew, Bernardo, had become expert marble players and had turned into professionals. They
usually wound up at the home of Epiphany, a chum living at
the farther end of the Alameda.

The ring where Epiphany and his visitors played was on the
hard ground beside Epiphany's home. The games were always
for "keeps." When luck would begin to go against Epiphany
he would start cheating. Then the fights between the boys
would begin. Although Epiphany was several years older than
either Estolano or Bernardo yet he would always run when
the two determined little marble shooters got after him.

The fight was just beginning. Epiphany's mother rushed on
the scene this particular night to take the part of her son. With
her broom she literally swept Estolano and Bernardo straight
out the front gate.

"There, Estolano, you little imp of Satan, get home," and
she gave the retreating figure a whack with her broom.

"And take Bernardo with you," she continued as she gave
this little urchin a similar slap on the seat of his pants.

Both went tumbling out the gate.

The two bewildered little fighters trudged forlornly up the
Alameda.

"I shan't go there any more," said the indignant Estolano.

"Me neither," said his nephew. "That's no way to treat visitors."

After the death of his father the ten-year-old Estolano had fast become a problem child. His mother soon could do nothing with him. He ran at will about the streets of San Juan. After school he would gamble with any boys that would play marbles with him. Oftentimes he did not get home to the Ranchito until long after dark. Finally a family conference was held, and it was decided to let Dolores have a free hand in straightening out the conduct of the little brother.

The Alameda, laid out in Mission Days, was a long dark road overshadowed on both sides by huge willow trees. It was a spooky place at night, especially when a person was passing under the third willow tree. A long horizontal branch grew out almost across the road. This was the limb on which in the early days the culprits of San Juan who weren't supposed to merit a trial were taken out and publicly hanged. As they passed homeward underneath this well known branch, Estolano hardly dared to look up, remembering still the sight of the body of the Indian boy that he had helped jiggle up and down.

The two little wanderers were just coming within sight of Adolfo Vache's tiny adobe store at the end of the Alameda. A faint candle light was shining through the checkered windows.

"Say, Bernardo," asked Estolano, trying to be cheerful, "wouldn't you like to have some Jenny Lind cookies?"

"Wouldn't I, though," said Bernardo.

"Have you got any money?"

"No."

"Me neither," said Estolano.

Bernardo and Estolano peered into the store, their noses pressed flat against the window panes.

"I've got a plan," whispered Estolano. "I'll go in and tell Mr. Vache my mother sent me to get some cookies."

Bernardo was surprised at the simplicity of his uncle's schemes. Already he could taste the Jenny Lind cookies, sweet like ginger snaps, but with no ginger in them. He waited discretely outside on the porch while his bold young uncle strode rather casually into the store.

"Good evening, Mr. Vache."

The French store keeper looked at him savagely.

"And what brings you down to my store so late at night?"

"My mother wants me to get a bag of Jenny Lind cookies."

"Estolano," thundered the little Frenchman, "you tell your mother I said for her to keep you home and off the streets at night."

Estolano took the hint. He went slinking out the door.

"Wouldn't he let you have any?" asked the disappointed Bernardo as the two continued their way along Third Street towards the Ranchito.

"Naw," said Estolano. "Guess he's all out of cookies."

There was a light in Aunt Pilar's house as the boys approached her well known adobe.

"If it wasn't so late," said Estolano thoughtfully, "we could stop in for a minute. Aunt Pilar is always glad to see me."

"But don't you see how dark it is getting," urged Bernardo. "You know," he added, "we have to pass the grave yards. And there isn't a bit of moonlight."

Both boys quickened their paces at the thought.

"Isn't it strange, Tio Estolano," said Bernardo, "that there isn't moonlight every night? Did you ever notice that some nights it is bright moonlight. You can see just like day. And other nights it is pitch dark. I wonder what makes the moon stay away part of the time."

"You've got me," said Estolano. "It must be that the moon isn't very dependable, very regular, Just comes out and shines when it wants to. When it don't want to shine it just stays—" Estolano was perplexed. "Well I don't know where it stays when it doesn't want to shine."

A couple of pickets were missing in the fence leading along the country road up to the Ranchito. By crawling through this opening and taking a path along the hillside it was shorter for the boys to reach the house, and besides they could escape having to walk so close along the graveyard fences.

"Not that I'm afraid," declared Estolano as he wriggled through the fence. "But I don't like to take chances. There might be ghosts there wandering around, you know."

Bernardo, two years younger than Estolano, followed his little uncle through the hole in the fence. When he was quite through he piped up: "Are ghosts only in cemeteries? I always supposed a person might see a ghost anywhere when it is dark."

The two boys walked along single file up the path. It was now very dark. Only the stars were shining. A pile of fence lumber had been left in the field for years. It was four feet high and was so close to the path that the boys could put their hands on it as they passed by. It stood out perfectly black in the darkness. But it was nothing to be afraid of, for they were perfectly familiar with it in the daylight.

Just as they were fairly well past this dangerous pile of lumber they heard the hoot of an owl seemingly right behind them.

"Hoot! Hoot!"

They were startled hearing the Hoot! so close to them. Both turned and looked backwards. It wasn't an owl.

Two ghosts were following them! One was about ten feet tall.

Like a bullet Estolano shot forward for home. Then remembering his nephew he stopped. The ghosts were still in sight in the distance. Braving them, he ran back and grabbed Bernardo by the hand. Together they ran ahead for at least a hundred yards. Bernardo gave out. He could run no farther. He fainted and fell to the ground. Estolano could neither get him up nor drag him.

Leaving the body of his nephew lying in the path, Estolano again ran forward at top speed for the Ranchito. When he reached the house he was too exhausted to utter a word. But by motions of his hands he made the men in the yard realize that he had left Bernardo behind somewhere along the trail. In alarm they hastened down and soon came back carrying Bernardo in their arms.

The joke had gone too far. There was great difficulty in reviving Bernardo. He was conscious but at every little rustle he would scream. All realized that something must be done to quiet Bernardo's nerves. In order to do this the men proceeded to show the boys who and what the ghosts were. The short one was Dolores. The other was a young man named Arroyo from the San Joaquin Ranch. He was the tall one. Both showed how they had wrapped bed sheets around themselves to make themselves look like ghosts. Arroyo had fastened his sheet on to a broom and held it above his head which made him look so tall.

"I wasn't a bit scared myself," declared Estolano to his mother after the excitement had died down. "But," he continued thoughtfully, "I think I will stay home nights after this. It isn't a good thing," the young rascal declared pompously, "for me to keep Bernardo out so late!"

The Mariano Castro Adobe Home of *Rose of the Rancho*

Chapter XXV

THE FALLON SCHOOL

SHORTLY AFTER the soldiers left San Juan in the spring of 1865 a school teacher by the name of Joseph King Fallon started a little private school in the Mission Corridors. He used the large room where the soldiers had had their tailor shop. It was about the third or fourth door from the end of the walk. Among his pupils were Estolano and his older brother, Patrocino, some of the Breen boys, Anatolio and Lupe Anzar and a few others. At the end of the summer the Fallons transferred their school to the country. They rented a large house and field in the Pajaro Valley, near Watsonville, from a man by the name of Bothwell. With their teacher went the Anzar boys and later Patrocinio.

Patrocinio, at the death of Don Manuel, was old enough legally to select his own guardian, and he chose Dr. MacDougall. Estolano's mother thought that it would be well for Estolano also to have a man to look after him.

"Estolano," she asked, "how would you like to have Dr. MacDougall for your guardian the same as Patrocinio and the Anzar boys?"

"I'd like it fine," promptly declared Estolano.

Whereupon papers were drawn up and signed, and Estolano became a ward of Dr. MacDougall. This Scotch Doctor was so highly esteemed in San Juan that he now had five of the richest

Spanish boys in San Juan as his wards. Dr. MacDougall promptly sent Estolano up to the Fallon school. Patrocinio had entered in the spring of 1866, and Estolano followed the same year after Christmas.

The house which the Fallons had rented from Bothwell was quite large. In it lived not only Mr. and Mrs. Fallon but their two daughters, Amelia and Jenny, aged twenty and twenty-two, a married son, Michael and his wife Delia, and a single man named William Gaffey. Amelia and Jenny were teaching country schools near home and used to set out every morning on their ponies for their respective schools. Jenny was a very lively young woman and to Estolano was perfectly adorable. Michael Fallon and Mr. Gaffey were running a dairy. They made butter and raised hogs. They would butcher the hogs and turn them into hams and bacon for the Watsonville market. Theirs was a flourishing business.

Four of the pupils at the Fallon school lived at a distance and had to come to school on horseback. Ned and Steve White were grown young men. The other two were Nellie Boyd and her younger brother who rode to school, the two on one horse. Other pupils lived within a mile and walked to school. The four boys from San Juan lived with the Fallon family. They were Anatolio, Lupe, Patrocinio and Estolano.

Mr. Fallon was an excellent teacher, and Estolano learned more arithmetic under him during the two years he was there than he had learned in all the previous years of his schooling. Mr. Fallon was also master of French and Spanish. Estolano took both. He did well in Spanish but not so well in French. Every single letter is sounded in Spanish, whereas in French Estolano found that oftentimes a full half of the letters are silent. This puzzled Estolano and gave him no end of trouble.

Estolano borrowed a nice little saddle nag from Amelia Fallon with which to make his first visit home to see his mother. During the night the horse strayed from the field at the Ranchito, where he had left it, and all the next day he searched for the animal in vain. Although Estolano had started out right after breakfast on a good horse and had looked in every nook and corner of the Ranchito, every part of which he knew so well, yet in all that day he had found no trace of the missing horse. It was now sunset, and he was making his way through the Alameda into San Juan. He had searched not only the Ranchito itself but he had even gone up into the San Juan Canyon. He was downhearted and forlorn. He could well afford to pay for the lost horse, but he knew that Amelia thought a great deal of old Lily and that several times the value of the horse would not recompense her for its loss.

But Estolano was not a person to give up. He still kept looking in every direction as he made his way back home. Glancing up a lane that led to a swampy place back of Faustino German's house, there to his astonishment he caught sight of old Lily. She was calmly grazing amid the luxuriant grass. Estolano spurred his horse and soon was leading Amelia's horse in triumph back to the Ranchito.

All the wards of Dr. MacDougall, except Estolano, had their own saddle horses. They also had muzzle-loading shotguns and rifles. But it was not long until Dr. MacDougall bought an ex-race horse for Estolano. This horse was from the Villegas Estate at Paicines and proved to be a dandy. Estolano was also allowed to purchase a gun for himself. From then on life for Estolano became one grand round of existence. Almost every afternoon after school he and Lupe, who were the greatest of chums, would go out hunting. They would bring back a bag full of quail and an occasional rabbit. Mrs. Fallon would turn these into the most savory of dishes and the four boys, Anatolio, Lupe, Patrocinio and Estolano, would fairly lick their chops as they sat down to supper.

The Fallon School was at the base of the Santa Cruz Mountains and about six miles east of Watsonville. The boys had

Saturdays and Sundays free. Tony and Pat would make arrangements with Ned and Steve White to go deer hunting over the week-ends, and Lupe and Estolano were always included in the gang. These six boys had a high time on these hunts. Mrs. Fallon would provide them with potatoes, onions, bread, salt, pepper, tea and coffee. The boys packed their blankets, provisions and cooking utensils on horseback. They would go straight east from the house about five or six miles to the summit of the mountains. There they pitched their camp and cooked their many quail stews and tenderloin venison steaks.

One afternoon instead of going out with Lupe on their daily quail hunt, Estolano went hunting with Anatolio. On their way home Anatolio pulled out a plug of black navy chewing tobacco. He bit off a chunk and passed the plug over to Estolano.

"Chew that, Estolano," declared Anatolio, "and it will make a man out of you."

Estolano did not need much persuasion. He bit off a sizeable chunk and began chewing it. When they reached home Tony proceeded to get washed for supper, but Estolano betook himself at once to bed. His head was dizzy, and he was so sick at his stomach. Good old Mrs. Fallon decided after a slight examination that Estolano had caught cold. Estolano let her think so, for he was ashamed to tell her that chewing tobacco was the real cause of his sickness. She immediately placed a big pinch of cayenne pepper in a tablespoon of milk and made Estolano swallow the dose. Shortly after he had swallowed the cayenne pepper he began to vomit. Mrs. Fallon was alarmed lest she had mixed the medicine too strong for him. She rubbed his temples soothingly, and finally Estolano pretended to sleep. Then she left him. The next morning Estolano was himself again, and Mrs. Fallon was delighted, believing that it was her old time remedies that had cured him in such short order.

The saddle horses always ran loose in the pasture. Lupe's

horse was almost pure white. He called it "Pichon," meaning Pigeon. He had it so trained that when he would blow his dog whistle the horse would come to him. Sometimes Lupe would play tricks on Pichon. He would hide behind some willows or other trees completely out of sight and then whistle. The horse would look up and then start walking in the direction from which he had heard the whistle, smelling his way carefully. No matter how thick the brush or trees were where Lupe was hiding, the horse would always find him. Estolano's horse, a piebald bay, was called "Tunante," meaning Cunning. He was too old to be taught much. But kindness and a lump of sugar would induce him to follow Estolano all over the yard. He would even come from the field when Estolano would call "Tunante." For this Estolano would pay him with either a lump of sugar or a handful of oats.

There was an earthquake while Estolano was at the Fallon school. Lupe and Estolano happened to be in the pasture at the time, to get their saddle horses. They had caught sight of them on the top of a long high hill. The boys went around the hill to the opposite side where the hill, though very much steeper, was a whole lot shorter to climb. When half way up the hill, Estolano saw Lupe who was in the lead begin to stagger and tumble. At the same time Estolano himself began to roll down the hill. He grabbed a bush and held fast. There was a small flat on top of the hill and a grove of pine trees growing there. Some were a foot through and better. The two startled boys could see these trees whipping the ground first to one side and then the other, like they were small switches being waved by some strong hand. For fully half a minute while the earthquake lasted, the boys hung to the bushes and watched the swishing trees. At the Fallon house several windows were broken. Dishes were thrown from the cupboard shelves and smashed.

Lupe had a well-trained Gordon setter dog, a splendid hunter and retriever. His name was Morengo. Estolano had a puppy from him. He called him Dandy and was training him to be like his father, Morengo. Anatolio also had a dog. It was a bull named Dick, not a thoroughbred but a good fighter, strong and tenacious. These three dogs were always with Lupe and Estolano on their jaunts about the school.

One day Lupe and Estolano with their ropes were after their horses in the pasture. The three dogs were with them. They could see the dogs running and barking along the board fence but they could not tell what they were chasing. Pretty soon they saw the dogs stop running and began jumping at something on the fence. It was a big wild cat. The boys had no gun with them, so they prepared to rope it. They got on opposite sides of the animal and began casting. Finally Lupe got his rope on it, and after a few more throws Estolano got his rope on the cat also. They pulled him off of the fence and dragged it home.

When they got to the house their next puzzle was what to do with the animal. First they stretched it out with their ropes. Then they tied one rope to the fence and the other to an old sycamore tree in the yard. They had dog collars galore. They cut one small enough to fit the animal and attached a long thin dog-chain to it. This collar they placed on the wild cat. They then took the cat up in the sycamore tree where a branch extended out over the roof of the dairy barn. They chained it to the branch of the tree in such a way that it could promenade on the roof of the dairy barn or perch on the limb of the tree.

They succeeded in raising a nice pet. After a few days he got so he would eat well and even became gentle. They took great pride in showing their cat to the visitors at the school. One man from Watsonville offered them five dollars for it. But they would not think of parting with their pet. One morning, however, when they went out to feed the cat its breakfast they found it dead. During the night it had attemped to jump down on the roof. But in doing so it had jumped the wrong way. It had leaped over an adjoining limb. The chain was too short for it to reach the roof, and there it hung choked to death.

Vache's Store

Chapter XXVI

SELLING QUAIL

IT WAS SIXTY-FIVE MILES from the Ranchito to the New Idria Mine. Estolano was home on a visit from the Fallon School and his brother Frank urged him to ride horseback with him to a dance at the mine. Frank had a sweetheart at the New Idria and was very anxious to see her. Estolano and Frank set out from the Ranchito at two o'clock in the morning. They had their breakfast at the home of David Watson who lived at *Agua Escondida* (Hidden Spring) about three miles up the Tres Pinos Creek from Paicines.

When the boys arrived at the New Idria about ten o'clock that night the dance was in full swing. Estolano, however, was completely played out. The trip was too much for him. Another brother, José, who was living at the mine at the time took him home and put him to bed. The joke was certainly on Estolano. All during the dance that he had come so far to attend he slept soundly. But Frank and his fiancée danced the whole night through and were still going strong at daylight the next morning.

Often on moonlight nights at the Fallon School Lupe and Estolano would go coon hunting. There was a little lagoon in the corner of an adjoining field. The north side of the pond was level and without any trees, while the south side was a steep wooded hill. They always went around the lower side first and then back through the woods. They were always accompanied by their three dogs, Morengo, Dandy and Dick. The dogs would trace and tree a coon. Then the boys would do the shooting. The meat they would take home for the chickens to eat. The skin they hung on the fence to dry.

One summer night Lupe and Estolano struck out for the pond. On this occasion the three dogs were running on ahead. Presently the boys knew from the way the dogs were barking that they had scared up something. The boys hurried on and soon came upon the three dogs fighting a badger. The dogs were unable to get a hold on the animal. Lupe had a shotgun while Estolano had only his revolver, a cap and ball five-shooter. For some time Lupe had not been able to shoot because of the dogs circling around the badger looking for a hold. Finally Lupe poked the muzzle of his gun right up against the badger's head and pulled the trigger. He gave it both barrels and killed it instantly. The boys then proceeded on their rounds, leaving the badger lying where they had found it.

On the hill near the east side of the lake the dogs again had something at bay. There on a fork of an oak tree the hunters saw a mountain lion gazing down at them and apparently just ready to jump. "Be ready with your pistol," commanded Lupe. "I'm going to give him both barrels right between the eyes." He shot. He split the lion's head as wide open as though it had been hit with a big cleaver. It fell to the ground and the dogs nabbed it. But the lion was already dead.

Later that night when Estolano was undressing he discovered that his pistol was gone. The next day when the boys went to skin the lion, they looked all around for the gun. They were unable to find it and finally gave up the search. Suddenly the idea came to Lupe to send Morengo to look for the gun. "Go find Estolano's pistol," he ordered Morengo. The dog seemed to understand. He backtracked running and hunting in all directions. In less than fifteen minutes back he came bringing the pistol in his mouth!

During the two summer vacations at the Fallon School the older boys, Anatolio, Lupe and Patrocinio, made many trips down to the San Lorenzo Valley after antelope. The country was full of wild game in those days. The boys would "wind up" a herd of antelope and chase them down on the floor of the valley. A large part of the valley was covered with wild oats, three and four feet high. The larger animals could make good time through these oats for they leaped ten and twelve feet at a bound and could keep it up for long stretches of time. But not so the young antelope. They would get tangled up in the oats and were easy prey for the sportsmen. The boys would capture them with their ropes.

Estolano made a trip to Sotoville after a horse that his brother Dolores had finished reining for him. Lupe accompanied him. Dolores lived in Sotoville. From Dolores' home Lupe and Estolano walked down to the business street a block away. The first building they came to was a saloon. As they stepped up on the front porch, a buggy drove up and stopped in front. The young man driving turned out to be a friend of Estolano's and they at once shook hands. Still sitting in the buggy was the father. This was the man whom Estolano had heard screaming the night Dr. MacDougall was cutting off his leg. The old Don now had no legs at all and only one arm. The son, Manuel, picked up his father bodily from the buggy seat, carried him into the saloon and sat him down upon the bar. The old gentleman was just as jolly as ever. In fact as he sat there helpless on the bar he was the liveliest person in the room.

The Fallons filed on a homestead for themselves about a mile farther out in the country and closer up to the hills. They built a commodious farm house which included a nice long school room. The Fallon family became much smaller by this time. Amelia had married William Gaffey, her brother's partner in the dairy business. They moved to San Francisco along with Michael Fallon and his wife Delia.

Lupe and Estolano were now left pretty much alone at the Fallon School. Ned and Steve White had been sent to Santa Clara College while Anatolio and Patrocinio went to Heald's Business College in San Francisco. But presently Dr. MacDougall sent his son, Fred, about nine years old, and a cousin, Antonio Figueroa, to the Pajaro school. The doctor also sent Mariano Castro, a cousin of Lupe and all the other members of the Castro family. Mariano was about twelve years old. One day he swore at Estolano.

"I'll fix you for that!" declared Estolano and he knocked Mariano down. Before Mariano could get up Estolano was firmly seated on top of him. He stretched Mariano's pants tight and then spanked him so violently that Mariano cried out in pain. In three or four days a big boil developed on the fleshy part of Mariano's anatomy, and he was unable for several days to take any comfort in sitting down.

The Fallon School was in the midst of a very jolly neighborhood. There were picnics and dances, here, there and everywhere. Lupe and Estolano never missed any, frequent though they were. On Saturday afternoon at the White school house there were the usual dancing lessons. Estolano did not learn much there, as he had learned at the Ranchito all the dances then extant. But Lupe and Estolano always had a nice time. A young lady named Mary Madden was staying with the Fallons. She and Jenny were always anxious to go to the dancing school. So Lupe and Estolano would hitch up the team of little mules to the spring wagon and together they would all go. Mary Madden would invariably appropriate Lupe who did the driving. That would leave poor Jenny in the back seat with Estolano. Lupe was about eighteen while Estolano was only thirteen. Jenny Fallon, however, was like a big sister to Estolano. He simply adored her.

After the school was moved to the new ranch, Lupe and Estolano did but little more quail shooting. Instead they built figure-four traps out of shakes and baited them with wheat. In these they caught the quail alive. They built a big coop and many times had upwards of a hundred birds in it.

Sam Sanborn worked as a clerk in the store of Ford and Sanborn in Watsonville. It was at this store that Lupe and Estolano did their trading, for Dr. MacDougall had arranged for them to have credit there. Young Sanborn used to come out in the country often hunting quail. He seldom got all the birds he wanted, so on his return he would stop at the Fallon School where the boys would sell him a dozen or two at a dollar a dozen. Sam also told others about Lupe and Estolano having quail for sale. By selling quail the boys managed to have a little extra spending money.

Lupe and Estolano were out deer hunting. They came upon a skunk disporting itself on a fallen log. Skunks are very pretty animals, jet black and usually with a white stripe down their backs. Lupe wanted to kill it and take the skin home for a curio. To shoot it was no trouble at all. The boys then tied a string to it and dragged it along behind them down the canyon to a place where there was water. Estolano held the skunk by the hind legs while Lupe proceeded to skin it. There was hardly any odor when they started in on the job, but as they progressed the smell became so sickening that they both began to vomit. They gave up skinning the animal and threw it away. But that didn't get them out of their difficulty. Although they washed and scrubbed their hands with sand and mud, it did no good. The more they tried to eradicate the smell, the stronger it became. They returned to their camp where they loaded up their camp equipment and started down the mountain for home. One horse was completely loaded, with the other they played ride and tie. That means ride and walk turn about. They got home about supper time and started to go into the house.

"Phew, whew!" exclaimed Mrs. Fallon, standing in the kitchen door. "Don't come in here."

Mrs. Fallon brought a complete change of clothing for the boys, but she would not come near them. She simply piled up everything in the yard where they could get it. Estolano and Lupe took their clothes and went to the creek about a hundred feet back of the house. They undressed and jumped into the water. They soaped themselves all over and washed thoroughly. Then after getting into their clothes they again presented themselves at the house.

Mrs. Fallon still wouldn't let them enter. She brought their supper outside on the porch and told them to take it out under the willows and eat by themselves. That night the boys of their own accord slept in the hay loft. The next morning when they washed for breakfast, they had one of the younger boys go to their room and bring them a bottle of Florida Water. It took the whole bottle to counteract the skunk odor. The embarrassed hunters were reluctantly admitted to the breakfast table and later to the school-room.

One day while visiting in San Juan, Estolano was going on horseback to call at the home of Doña Rufina Castro, the mother of the "Rose of the Rancho," who was also the mother-in-law of Dr. MacDougall. A team of horses hitched to a buggy came tearing down the Alameda on the dead run. In the buggy was a young man and a young woman. The thing that occurred to Estolano to do was to unfasten his rope and then stand waiting on the side of the road. As the team passed him, he spurred his horse up close to the runaway team and threw the rope over the heads of the two horses. He took a couple of turns around the saddle horn and began gradually to check the speed of the team. He knew that if he gave them a sudden hard pull there would be an upset and a general smash.

By the time the racing horses had reached the old Adolfo Vache store, he had them under control. Several men rushed out of the store and grabbed the horses by the bits. The occupants of the buggy got out. The girl was Catherine Breen and the young man was a visitor from San Francisco. The stranger forced a ten dollar gold piece into Estolano's hand.

"You are a wonderful boy, Estolano. You not only knew what to do, but what is more, you went right ahead and did it."

The men from the store pulled Estolano off his horse and carried him into the small adobe *cantina*. They stood him up on the bar and showered him with soda water and candy galore. Estolano felt quite proud of himself, for he was only a boy of thirteen at the time.

Estolano once made a trip to San Juan, going straight over the mountains by way of the Aromas Ranch. He was with Sam Mathews, a young man who had been his school-mate in San Juan. At the present time Sam had charge of a band of sheep belonging to his father, and had a little cabin in the mountains eight or ten miles beyond the Fallon School. Lupe and Estolano often visited him. Sam Mathews was riding past the Fallon School and invited Estolano to go with him to San Juan. With Mr. Fallon's consent he did so. He rode Tunante, the old race horse. Sam was riding a young roan horse, quite active and pretty.

Just before descending the last hill leading down to the Pajaro River, they came upon a small bunch of cattle on a little tableland. Among them was a young two-year-old bull. Sam proposed that they try their hand lassooing it. He offered to bet that he could get his rope on it first. Undoing their riatas they soon cut out the bull and started after it. Estolano's old horse had not forgotten his racing days. Tunante overtook the bull first, and Estolano threw his rope on it. It was quite a tussle for Estolano to hold the animal until Sam could come up and catch it by the feet. Then they stretched the bull out. It was now up to Sam to hold the bull until Estolano could dismount and remove his rope from the animal's head.

Estolano's rope was hardly off when Sam slackened his line and let the bull up. This was before Estolano could get back on his horse. The bull was between Estolano and Tunante and by then was pretty mad. It did not take Estolano long to decide what to do. There was a little dry gulch about a hundred yards down-grade. Estolano knew that his only chance to escape the bull was to run and jump into the gulch out of the bull's reach. Estolano was fleet-footed. He ran with all his might. The bull was following right behind him. He could feel his hot breath on his back. The gulch was deep and narrow. Estolano plunged in just in the nick of time. The bull jumped right over him and kept on its way.

Sam was almost rolling off his horse with laughter. Estolano on regaining his horse, first used up all the cuss words he knew in English, which was plenty. Then he switched over into Spanish where the swear words are twice as hot. He told Sam plainly what he thought of him, letting the bull up before he was back on his horse. The only thing that prevented a fight was because Sam was almost a grown man and too big for Estolano to tackle.

The two horsemen proceeded on their way. As they rode along Estolano cooled off by degrees and, the funny side of the situation dawning on him, he joined Sam in laughter. On arriving in San Juan they separated as good friends as ever.

Chapter XXVII

ESTOLANO BECOMES A SHEEP HERDER

THE YOUNGER BOYS wanted to go to a little lake a mile or so up the hill from the Fallon School. Estolano, who was now one of the big boys at the school, offered to take the little fellows up. After rounding the lake they continued their walk along the cattle trail that wound along the side of a steep canyon. They had not gone more than a quarter of a mile when they met a band of cattle, eight or ten in number, coming down the trail on a keen run and headed straight for the Fallon school boys. A big savage steer was in the lead. In order to keep the cattle from running over them, Estolano, who had his little five-shooter with him, fired point blank at the leader who turned headlong down the side of the canyon followed by the rest of the band.

On reaching home, the boys told of their experience and how Estolano had held his ground, firing off his revolver and saving the day. Not long after that a man named Pat Kelly who owned a ranch and had cattle in the neighborhood came down to the school and began quizzing the boys.

"Yes sir," bragged Estolano. "I sure drove those cattle out of our way."

"You are certainly a good marksman," declared Mr. Kelly. "You shot my steer squarely between the eyes. It is now lying dead at the bottom of the canyon. Young man, you must pay me thirty dollars for my steer."

Estolano was dumbfounded. He went in the house and sought out his teacher. Mr. Fallon came out and talked with Kelly. Finally a compromise was effected and Mr. Fallon handed a twenty dollar gold piece to Mr. Kelly. Later Dr. Mac-Dougall paid this out of Estolano's share of Don Manuel's estate.

Estolano rode home one day on a visit to his mother. Arriving at the Ranchito, he found living there in place of his mother, Mrs. Crane and her family of three daughters. On inquiring, he found that his mother had sold the Ranchito and was living temporarily with Juan Antonio, her oldest son. Thither he repaired. All were glad to see him, but his mother urged him to go right back to Watsonville. She told him not to go into San Juan at all, for the smallpox was raging there and people were dying every day. So Estolano returned at once to the Pajaro.

When Estolano reported the epidemic, Mrs. Fallon was alarmed and at once ordered the little team of mules hitched up. She piled all the boys then in school into the wagon and set out for Dr. Ford in Watsonville to have them vaccinated. There were three young lads beside Lupe and Estolano. The latter drove the team and Lupe rode along on horseback. All were vaccinated. Later when the smallpox struck Watsonville the Fallons wrote to Dr. MacDougall who had moved to Los Angeles that it would be better for all the boys to go home, as the Fallons could not care for them if they came down with the smallpox. Dr. MacDougall promptly wrote for all the boys to pack up and leave. Mariano Castro and Tony Figueroa were sent to their home ranches near San Juan, while Lupe, Fred MacDougall and Estolano were told to go to the Aromas Ranch. They were to stay with Pedro Marentes who was foreman at the ranch for Dr. MacDougall.

Lupe and Estolano took their dogs and horses home with them and also a glow worm they had picked up one night on their return from Watsonville. The glow worm looked something like a caterpillar but was more flat and not hairy. It was better than two inches long and fully half an inch wide. It had black and white stripes all along its body. The white stripes emitted the light. They kept it in a little glass jar. They fed it green leaves, principally elder. The light from the glow worm was so strong that the boys could distinguish printed words when held close to the jar in the dark.

Estolano became tired of staying at the Aromas Ranch. He wanted to go home to his mother. After two or three weeks one morning he got on his horse and rode straight into San Juan. He found his mother this time living with her daughter, Juana. The Belardez family had a little lumber house near the east fence of the Ranchito on a flat knoll. This knoll had been the battle ground between the North and the South during the school battles of the Civil War. With Juana were her two sons, Juan and Bernardo, the latter of whom had been Estolano's boon companion in his marble-shooting days.

The smallpox was raging in San Juan. The whole town had been exposed, and now nothing could be done about it but to let the plague run its course. The boys occasionally went into town; but whenever they were passing a house that had a white flag flying from the gate, they would hold a piece of camphor gum to their nose and run with all their might.

On one occasion, however, Estolano stopped in where a white flag was flying. He wanted to see a very dear friend of his, named Miguel, whose mother was Gertrudes, an Indian girl raised in the Larios family whom Don Manuel had picked up in the San Joaquin Valley after a raid on the Santa Ana Ranch. Miguel was in bed with the smallpox and Gertrudes would not let Estolano in the house. But Estolano forced his way through the door in spite of her. Miguel recognized Estolano, and the two boys bade each other farewell. In less than three days Miguel was buried.

The Belardez home was about three hundred feet from the graveyard. Burials were made only at night. There were no funerals, and the boxes containing the bodies were buried without any ceremonies of any kind. Bodies were brought to the cemetery at all times of the night. Often before going to bed, while sitting out of doors in the cool of the evening, Estolano and his two nephews would hear the clods of dirt falling on the home-made coffins as the victims of the plague were being buried. It was a dismal sound and very depressing to the three young boys. Estolano pondered long. He wished that he could do something for the people of San Juan. He wished that he was a doctor.

While Estolano and his mother were staying at the Belardez home, a bunch of hogs belonging to "Pongle, Don," kept coming up and getting into a pile of corn that was stored back of the house. It was fenced in only by a wall of pumpkins which the hogs had no difficulty in rooting out of their way. One morning Estolano and his two nephews drove four or five of the hogs out of the corn just as they had done dozens of times before. But this particular morning Estolano was armed with Don Manuel's old army lance that stood in a corner of his mother's room. He was planning to get close enough to the hogs to give one of them a jab as they went single file through a gap in the fence on their way to the road. Estolano arrived just in time to let fly at the last one, a big fat sow. The lance struck her along the side of her ribs. She squeeled and made a few turns in a circle. The lance dropped to the ground and she toppled over. Pongle, Don lived about three blocks away, and his sons happened to be coming for the hogs at the time. They saw what Estolano had done and reported it to their father. Pongle, Don, came at once to see Mrs. Larios and demanded that she pay him ten dollars for the hog that Estolano had killed.

"All right," said she, "I'll give you ten dollars, but I'll take the pig."

"No," said Pongle, Don in astonishment. "The hog is mine. I'll keep it. And you must pay me ten dollars besides."

"No," said Mrs. Larios, equally emphatic. "I'll buy the pig of you. Or you can butcher the hog for yourself. I'll not pay you one cent on any other condition."

Pongle, Don went home without any money. His family had fresh pork for several days. But he kept his hogs home after that.

The smallpox continued to rage in San Juan, and Mrs. Larios decided that she and Estolano had better move to the Black Hill, between Tres Pinos and Paicines, distant about eighteen miles from San Juan. Juanito, her son, had a little store there and a small dwelling. The Black Hill was on the road to the New Idria mine. Mrs. Larios hired Trinidad German, a nephew, to come with a four horse wagon and haul everything up to Juanito's ranch. In a short time she had her own house finished, and they moved across the road from Juanito's.

Trinidad German soon after came down with the smallpox. Juanito had had the disease in an earlier epidemic. So he made a hospital out of one of his store rooms and took care of Trinidad. Pretty soon, Sylvester Durfee, who had been working at the Belardez ranch came to Juanito's store with all the symptoms of smallpox. That made two in Juanito's hospital. Presently a little niece, Angelita Barcelon, a girl of about ten years, was brought over from her home. She had the bad type, the black smallpox. She died, and they buried her on the hillside.

Estolano and his nephew, Bernardo Belardez, went up on the hill one day on foot to get Estolano's horse which was running with Juanito's bellmare. It was very hot weather, and the boys had a long climb and chase after the horses. When they got home both had a headache and backache, the dreaded symptoms of smallpox. Estolano's mother spread a blanket on the floor in the front room for them to sleep on, and at once began to administer emetics. The next morning early she gave both boys a large dose of castor oil.

Estolano overheard the folks saying in the kitchen that if the boys were not better by evening they must be taken to the hospital. Estolano made up his mind right then and there that he would not under any circumstances go to the hospital. He dressed and started outdoors.

"I'm not sick, mother. In fact I feel pretty well."

Such was not the case. He felt miserable. But he had such a dread of Juanito's hospital that talk as she might his mother could not persuade him to go back to bed. That night Bernardo was carried bed and bedding across the road to the hospital. But in three days Estolano had perfectly recovered, cured as he firmly believed by his will to be well.

Fall shearing had started at the Buena Vista Ranch. A number of men and boys from the Black Hill went up there looking for work. Estolano was one of them. The Buena Vista Ranch belonged to Don Estanislao Hernandez. There were two bands of sheep in the field adjoining the shearing pens, and Estolano asked Hernandez to give him a job herding. The sheep man only laughed.

"You can't stand the work," he told Estolano. "The walking would be too much for you.

But Estolano persisted.

"Well," finally weakened Hernandez, "you can use your horse and help the other herder. Come down to the headquarters here for your meals."

Estolano started right in and liked the work very much. But he had been working only a week when Lupe Anzar came up from the Aromas Ranch looking for him. When Estolano came down the hill to get his dinner, Lupe handed him a letter from Dr. MacDougall. In it Estolano's guardian directed him to take the stage as soon as possible for Santa Barbara where he was to enter the Franciscan College at the Old Mission.

Mr. Hernandez smiled when Estolano told him that he would have to quit. He already knew that Lupe, who was Señor Hernandez' Godson, had come to take Estolano away, for Lupe had told him while they were waiting for Estolano to come down to dinner. Hernandez pulled out a ten dollar gold piece and handed it to Estolano as his wages. He then gave him some fatherly advice:

"I am glad, Estolano, that you are not ashamed to turn an honest dollar. But you must fit yourself for something better than a sheep herder. Your father left you plenty of money to do with. You must study hard at college and make something worth while out of yourself."

Don Estolano Larios, 1938

. . . and his calling card

SPANISH

 The beautiful idiom of "Cervantes"
The future language for "Young America"

Easily Acquired ∿ Taught by New and Original Methods

Will give lessons in classes or singly if preferred
For particulars, see other side.

E. F. LARIOS, Oregon City, Oregon

(over) (R.2 Box 2A), Brick House on Abernathy Road

TERMS:

For 2 lessons a week
  In class room . . . . $5, per m.

At your own home
  any time you set . "6, " "

At my home
any time not taken
up with other classes "4, " "

Reading - Writing - Translating
guaranteed in six months. General conversation in one year.

Phone 745
  Oregon City Business College
  or communicate with

E. F. LARIOS

Chapter XXVIII

STAGING

IT WAS WITH mingled feelings of uneasiness and resentment that Estolano waited at the Plaza Hotel in San Juan for the arrival of the big Flint and Bixby stage coach for Santa Barbara. Estolano felt that he was being torn up by the roots as it were from his home, his friends and everything that he had ever known in life. He didn't want to go to college. He was half resolved to defy his guardian and refuse to leave San Juan.

Soon however the big four horse stage came rolling in past the General Castro house and abruptly stopped in front of the Plaza Hotel. The sense of movement revived momentarily his spirits. Johnny Comfort, the agent of the Stage Company, quickly assigned him a seat in the coach and told him to climb aboard. The conductor examined his ticket and punched holes in various places in the long strip of paper. Estolano's trunk, no longer in his possession, was quickly stowed away in the boot. But the fourteen-year-old boy held back the tears with difficulty, as he gazed out the coach window and saw his mother standing there in front of the hotel all alone. Estolano felt for the moment that he was running away from his duty rather than performing bravely the task that was his.

The stage driver sent the four horses at a fast lope down the road. Estolano had a last fleeting glance at the Ranchito house. Over the hills the stage went to Natividad. Late in the evening they were at the El Pluto Stage Station where the coach stopped for supper. This consisted principally of stale jerky venison. Estolano had no appetite, and this tasteless supper made him feel all the more forlorn. All night the stage swayed and rocked. The leather thoroughbraces oftentimes let the stage bounce so high that Estolano's head would strike the ceiling of the coach. Before morning his head was one mass of bumps and bruises from the many times his head had struck the sides and top during the night.

At noon the next day Estolano's nose was beginning to bleed, and he was unable to get it stopped. At a stage station a fellow passenger put a half dollar in some cold water and then pressed it on the back of Estolano's neck. At the same time this friend doubled up several thicknesses of paper soaked in cold water and put them under Estolano's lip. To Estolano's surprise the bleeding stopped. The stage then rolled on.

The horses went on a keen lope day and night. At four that afternoon, just twenty-four hours after leaving San Juan the stage passed through San Luis Obispo. The next morning, after two sleepless nights for Estolano, the stage rolled into Santa Barbara.

On getting off the stage, Estolano was at a loss to know just what to do. He remembered José Espinoza, the cowboy who used to whistle for the dances at the Ranchito. He believed that Espinoza was then living in Santa Barbara. He decided to try and find him. Maybe José would help him get his trunk out to the college.

First Estolano rented a room for himself at a lodging house. He wanted to "make camp" as it were before he sallied forth.

Immediately after lunch Estolano set out to find José. Approaching a bartender leaning against a post in front of a small saloon, he asked:

"Do you know a Spanish fellow by the name of José Espinoza?"

"Do I!" exclaimed the young man. "Why he was my brother."

Estolano soon learned to his sorrow that José was dead. His widow, Refugio Butron, and her three children were living with the grandmother. The bartender showed Estolano where the house was and he went to call. Doña Refugio was both surprised and delighted to see him. Estolano in turn was delighted to find someone he knew.

That afternoon there was going to be a cock fight in the yard back of the Espinoza saloon and the bartender who had come to the house to get his fighting cock invited Estolano to come with him and watch it.

A crowd collected in the back yard and a judge was chosen. The spectators formed a ring about twelve feet in diameter. Espinoza had a steel gaff, sharp as a razor. It was shaped like a rooster's spur and was about two or three inches long. This he securely fastened to the rooster's leg where the spur should be. Espinoza's rooster was a little game cock well trained for fighting.

The owners of the two roosters that were to take part in the fight acted as coaches, holding the roosters opposite each other face to face. When the birds showed fight by erecting their neck feathers, each coach in turn said "Ready." The judge ordered "Go!" and the roosters were turned loose.

The birds knew their business and, like well-trained pugilists, kept sparring around for an opening. Suddenly they flew at each other, using their spurs at the same time. Espinoza's rooster was ripped wide open from the breast down. The other got a mortal wound on the side of the neck.

Each coach picked up his rooster and placed it again in the center of the ring face to face with its antagonist. Both birds were bleeding profusely and were dying. The Espinoza rooster erected its neck feathers, which in rooster parlance means, "I'll fight!" The other rooster showed no fight at all. Its neck feathers never came up. The judge gave the decision to Espinoza, along with the twenty-five dollar side bet. Both men then cut off their roosters' heads. After treating the crowd, Espinoza set out for home, taking Estolano with him for a forced chicken dinner.

Chapter XXIX

"HELLO, SQUINT"

THE NEXT FORENOON Estolano spent the time on the water-front. He was admiring the sea-going ships in the harbor. They were so much larger than he had ever dreamed ships would be. He went on board one that was tied up to the wharf. It seemed as large as the Ranchito house itself. He was having such a good time looking out over the ocean and running around on the dock that he didn't care if he ever got to college.

A hack drove up to the dock and a middle aged, bare headed man, clad in a long gray gown, climbed down from the driver's seat. It was Brother Richard from the Old Mission. One of his duties was to drive the hack belonging to the college. He had been sent to round up Estolano and get him out to the school. Estolano watched the strangely dressed man who was walking directly over to him.

"Aren't you that boy from San Juan Bautista who came in on the stage yesterday?"

"Yes sir," said Estolano very respectfully.

"Then why aren't you out to the college where you belong?"

"I don't know where the college is," pleaded Estolano in excuse.

"Well," declared the man in deep Irish brogue, "you didn't think the college would be out here on the waterfront, did ye? Get in the hack and I'll take you out."

It was Wednesday when Estolano arrived at the college. The next morning Father O'Keefe took him to his class-room and proceeded to examine him thoroughly. Estolano had brought some of his old school books with him. He had *Wilson's Sixth Reader* and a *New York Standard Speaker*. In place of these Father O'Keefe furnished him with a *Metropolitan Reader*, which Estolano found quite difficult. After selecting several other books for Estolano Father O'Keefe found a seat for him in the study hall along with the other boys.

There were about one hundred and seventy-five students in the Franciscan College. Some fifty of them were Spanish Californians. Father Gonzales was the Superior and Father Sheehan the President. The principal teachers were Father Wade and Father O'Keefe. Father Coffey, a Jesuit, taught languages. The Prefects were Brothers John Callinan and John Reid. They taught the lower grades.

Thursday afternoons were recreation days for the students. After lunch it was customary for the whole school to go for a walk through the woods back of the Mission grounds. The students were required to look presentable when leaving the Mission. All repaired to the wash rooms and from there to the trunk-room to change their clothes, if they desired to do so. Estolano unlocked his trunk with a view to putting on a clean shirt and tie. Father O'Keefe came and stood beside Estolano. He picked up a coat lying in the trunk.

"That's nice goods," he remarked. "What did you pay for it?"

He kept picking up article after article, commenting on their quality and asking their cost. Estolano was beginning to get nervous.

Father O'Keefe finally got to the very bottom of the trunk. The priest was astonished. There he found ten plugs of chewing tobacco, two cans of cigars and one hundred and fifty packages of cigarettes! He asked if the stuff was Estolano's and if he used it himself.

"Yes, it is all mine," confessed the young Don, "and I use it."

Father O'Keefe told him that it was against the rules of the school to use tobacco in any form, shape or manner.

"I'll take charge of all this, and when you are leaving you can call on me for it. You are not to use tobacco while you are here."

This was quite a set-back to the upkeep of Estolano's already acquired bad habits.

When the boys were returning from their walk that first afternoon Estolano was walking along with three other Spanish boys, Dario Oreña, Osvaldo de la Guerra and Ramundo Olivas. Behind them were three or four American boys. Among them was Gustavus Coleman, a boy probably fifteen or sixteen years old, heavily built, but not as tall as Estolano. They had acorns in their pockets and were pelting the Spanish boys with them. Most of the acorns were aimed at Estolano. One acorn hit on the ear and stung pretty bad.

"Whoever did that had better stop it," shouted Estolano to Coleman.

Pretty soon, as if in derision, a whole handful of acorns hit Estolano on the back. He rushed back straight for Coleman. The American ran but Estolano tripped him, sending him sprawling. Estolano gave him a blow on the cheek and would have done better but Ramundo warned Estolano:

"Let him up. Here comes the priest."

Father O'Keefe was catching up with them. All walked meekly away towards the playground. But the row was not over.

After supper a young Irish boy named Ignacio Glynn, who knew all about the afternoon racket, started picking on the new student. Estolano didn't need much of this to urge him on. Fortunately he could handle his fists in very fair fashion.

A ring was formed, coats peeled and at it they went. After the first round the alarm was sounded and the crowd dispersed. Estolano picked up his coat and walked over to a corner of the yard where his Spanish friends were. The boys said that Glynn had gone over to the wash-room to wash up a bloody nose. The next day Glynn showed up in the school room with quite a nice swollen eye.

Sunday evening after supper there was a crowd of boys gathered about the swing and rings. Estolano was on the rings just starting up. Nelson Beck, about eighteen years old, was passing in front of him and Estolano accidentally bumped him. Beck turned and grabbed Estolano off the rings. Estolano expected that Beck would simply demolish him. In the scuffle, however, Estolano got his forefinger inside Beck's mouth and his thumb under his jaw. With his left hand in his coat collar and with a heavy kick on the side of the ankle, Mr. Nelson was brought flat on his back. Estolano lifted him by the top-knot and giving him a good swift paste on the jaw sent him sprawling again. Beck limped into the school room, and the next morning didn't attend early Mass. Instead he sat on the church steps with his ankle all bandaged up.

In the school study hall the students sat on long benches. On the left of Estolano sat Jerry Mullens who was a cripple. Jerry was about eighteen years old, but had only one good leg. The other was a dwarfed leg about like an eight or ten year old boy, caused probably from infantile paralysis. He had a contrivance attached to the leg and could walk pretty well. He could also swim. Late one afternoon, returning from a walk, the boys were all in the study hall. Estolano was wearing a long-tailed coat. Jerry put his foot up on the bench on top of Estolano's coat-tail. Gently removing Jerry's leg he told Jerry he was soiling his coat. Again Jerry's foot found its way on top of Estolano's coat-tail. Estolano then gave the foot a hard shove. With that Jerry smashed Estolano squarely in the eye.

In self defense Estolano grabbed Jerry by the collar, pushed him down between the bench and the desk and then gave him a punch on the mouth and nose. Immediately Ignacio Glynn, who sat directly behind, jumped up and struck Estolano a terrific jolt on the back of the head. Then Francisco Noreiga, a big Spanish boy, took Estolano's part and engaged Glynn. Instantly John O'Keefe, a twenty-two-year-old man and brother of Father O'Keefe tackled Noreiga. By that time Prefect Brother John Cullinan was on the scene and gave O'Keefe a cut across the shoulders with his rattan. That reestablished order.

It was the duty of the Prefect to put the names of those misbehaving on the slate, together with their offense. Just before school was dismissed each day President Sheehan came in and looked over the slate. Estolano was the first one called on the carpet. Although he pleaded self defense, he received three rather sharp strokes on the palm of his right hand with a two-inch hard rubber ruler. Estolano thought the punishment undeserved. Through madness he didn't cry out, though he suffered intense pain. Jerry was then called. He admitted all that Estolano had said. He also received three hard cuts on the hand with the ruler. Although he did not whimper, big tears were rolling down his cheeks as he returned to his seat. None of the other participants in the melee were called.

For several days after the boys would tease Jerry by saying:

"Hello, Jerry. Where did you get that mug?"

Jerry's teeth had cut his upper lip, and it had swelled up almost even with his nose.

Estolano's eye, on his part, was swelled almost shut and the boys would call out:

"Hello, Squint!"

The Original Church Door

Chapter XXX

FRANCISCAN COLLEGE

THE REFECTORY was on the ground floor of the Monastery. The meals were good, substantial and plentiful. Breakfast consisted of rolled oats or corn meal, served with plenty of milk and sugar. Coffee and cream with bread and butter were included. For dinner there was always good soup made out of rice, macaroni, pearl barley or vermicelli. There was roast beef, potatoes and other vegetables, with dried apple or peach pie for dessert. Supper was generally beef stew. Now and then the boys were served nice roast mutton with the general run of vegetables. For dinner the drink was water. For supper there was tea. The winter months were sometimes hard on the boys for their desserts were dried fruits. But throughout the summer when fresh fruit was in season, they were served fresh fruit twice a day. The fruit consisted principally of oranges and grapes with plenty of muskmelons and watermelons. Fridays, throughout the year, they had only codfish stew for dinner and codfish balls for supper. During the Lenten season the boys were required to abstain from flesh on Wednesdays and Fridays. During Holy Week this rule followed every day. However, through Lent they had fresh fish often.

The school had plenty of milk and eggs. Father José was the *factotum.* He had half a dozen cows to milk, a few sheep to tend and lots of chickens. On Easter Sunday eggs were served special, and a person could have a dozen if he could eat that many.

The entire second floor of the Monastery was given over to the Franciscan College proper. The study hall was on the west end of the building. Along the front facing towards Santa Barbara were the class rooms. There were two dormitories, one for the big boys and one for the little fellows. Tuition, including board and washing, was one hundred and fifty dollars for a term of ten and a half months. Music lessons, piano, violin, flute or cornet, were five dollars per month extra. French and German and Spanish lessons were three and a half per month with two lessons a week. Father O'Keefe taught piano, while Brother John Cullinan taught the violin, flute and cornet. Father Romo, a Castillian priest, taught Spanish. Father Coffey, who was an Irishman, taught French and German. He was a short, corpulent man and was a Jesuit, the only one in the institution. He wore the Jesuit habit instead of the Franciscan.

Brother John Cullinan, who was the violin teacher, had found an old broken violin that had been used by the Indians in the early days of the Mission choir. He patched it up nicely and used it right along, declaring it was the best violin he ever played. Brother John was an old-time violinist and had led an orchestra in the California Theater in San Francisco for many years.

Father Coffey had received his schooling in the old country and spoke pure Parisian French. Some of his pupils he would keep for days on the pronunciation of just two words, *monsieur* and *sucre.* The "u" in these words has a sort of whistling sound, and he would keep the pupils at it until they got the sound just right. He was fastidious and touchy. Few of the boys liked him. Gaspar de la Guerra was one of his pupils. He stole a side of codfish from the store-room and hid it behind the class-room door. When Father Coffey came in he smelled the disagreeable odor.

"Phew! Phew!" he sniffed.

All the boys began laughing. This made him angry, and he dismissed the class without hearing a lesson. On another occasion Father Coffey stepped into his room which adjoined the class-room and, on returning to his desk, found his glasses missing. He was so out of patience he again dismissed the class. All the boys were laughing uproariously, for the Father did not know that his glasses were on his forehead where he had pushed them up out of the way and forgotten them. As the boys were going out of the door, Estolano suggested to the Father that he feel on top of his head. The little Irish priest laughed at the joke on himself, called the boys back and the lesson proceeded.

It was the custom of the school on the evening of the last day of each month to appoint two boys to read aloud in the Refectory at dinner and at supper. The reader had an elevated parapet seat and desk against the south wall midway the length of the dining-room. There were twelve tables in the dining room, four tables along the walls on each side and two tables at each end. Father Wade sat at one end table near the middle of the wall. Brother John Cullinan sat at the other end. When either of them saw a boy talking or not paying attention, he would sound the bell for silence. The reader would stop. Then Father Wade would ask the offender what the reader had last said. If the boy did not know, he got a black mark. Three of these marks would bring the deserved punishment. This being the case, the boys generally behaved well, ate quietly and listened attentively to the reading. Charlie de la Guerra was the best reader in the Refectory. He had a clear articulation and a stentorian voice. The readers for the month would change about weekly. One read at noon and the other read at night. The passages selected were usually historical and were on thoughtful subjects.

Reveille was at five-thirty in the morning. Early Mass was

at six o'clock. Breakfast was at seven. At eight-thirty school opened and at nine recitations began. There was a half hour recess at ten. At a quarter to twelve school was out for noon. Dinner was at twelve. School began at one o'clock. A thirty-minute recess followed at two o'clock and at four o'clock school was out for the day. Supper was at six o'clock. An hour of study was held, beginning at half past seven. Prayers followed in the study hall and then bed at nine.

Recreation days were Thursdays and Sundays. There were no recitations Thursday forenoons, but the boys were required to study until the noon meal. After dinner they went out for a walk in the country or had a baseball game. Sunday, after attending church services, was recreation all day long.

At the monthly meeting of the faculty the acolytes to serve Mass with each priest were named for the month, two to each priest. That meant sixteen boys, for there were eight priests who said Mass. There were nine altars in the church. The main altar was occupied by Father Gonzales, the Superior of the College. There were altars on each side of the confessional below the main altar and three altars on each side of the walls of the church. The boys would hurrah when they were selected to serve either Father Sanchez or Father Alvarez. The former would always leave half or more in the vial containing the wine for consecration, while Father Alvarez always left two-thirds or three-quarters of it. The boys that served them would regale themselves with this wine when returning to the sacristy.

Every Roman Catholic boy was required to go to confession and receive communion regularly the first of every month. During Lent and Holy Week this was done weekly. Although required to abstain from flesh, they were not obliged to fast. That was left to their own discretion.

An Italian by the name of José Lobero organized a band in Santa Barbara of thirty or more members. The band became very efficient and played beautifully. On one church holiday Lobero's band was engaged to play in the choir at the Mission. It was the only time that Estolano ever heard a brass band play in a Roman Catholic choir at church services.

On this same occasion in the open space in front of the Mission a series of little brush houses had been erected in circular form, each *enramada* containing a holy image on an altar. After the services in the church were concluded the principal celebrant, followed by the assisting Friars, all in their vestments, walked in procession carrying the Holy Eucharist. In front of the procession walked six little girls dressed in white with crowns of flowers on their heads and carrying baskets filled with flower petals, which they strewed along the path of the head priest. During the march the band, drawn up in front of the Mission, played appropriate airs. The whole affair was thrilling and impressive to Estolano.

There were rims around the belfry of the church towers about twenty inches wide. Some of the boys used to play tag up there. They would run around these rims as though they were on level ground. An elderly man who had been the bell ringer in the tower was kept on a pension by the Fathers. One time when ringing the bells the rope broke, and he fell to the stone steps below and was crippled for life. This accident, however, didn't deter the boys from their sport.

On Sundays and other church holidays the church would be filled with people, principally from town. There were many pretty girls in Santa Barbara. Crowds of them would attend services at the Mission and then linger outside, attracted by the many boys upstairs in the Monastery. This gave the boys the finest kind of opportunity to carry on handkerchief flirtations from the many windows in the study hall and even from the bell towers. These flirtations were carried on with the greatest animation. A boy drawing his handkerchief across his lips meant that he was desirous of an acquaintance with the girl watching him from below. Drawing it across his cheek meant "I love you." A girl resting her handkerchief on her right cheek signaled "Yes." Holding his handkerchief by the opposite corners in both hands meant "Wait for me." Putting away his handkerchief in his pocket told the girl "No more at present."

Chapter XXXI

RECREATION DAYS

THE STUDENTS at the Franciscan College went in sets. Each boy belonged to his own clique or gang. One crowd consisted of twelve Spanish boys. There were the three de la Guerra boys, Carlos, Gaspar and Osvaldo, all cousins. There were also the three Oreña brothers, Leopoldo, Dario and Orestos. Two Pacheco brothers were named Ramuldo and Juan. Then there were Francisco Noriega, Ramundo Olivas, Orel Goldarcena and Estolano. The *factotums* were Ramuldo Olivas and Gaspar de la Guerra. These two boys would get up at all hours of the night and silently leave the dormitory. Each took a pillow-case with him. They would walk a mile through the woods up to the vineyards and orange grove. There they would fill their pillow-cases with a goodly load of grapes or oranges and then cache them along the creek where the gang had its rendezvous. These forays were always on Wednesday or Saturday nights. The following day being "recreation," the gang would repair to their rendezvous and enjoy a feast. The boys often had nice cookies, cheese and such dainties, brought up from town by day scholars the day before, and so enjoyed a regular picnic. Often the two *factotums* would raid Father José's chicken house and wring the heads off of a couple of fat hens. The boys would draw them and then later roll the chickens in clay until they were coated with mud at least an inch thick. The cooks would build a good fire and when the coals and hot ashes were ready they would bury the chickens in the hot ashes. When the clay fell apart the chickens were done. The feathers and skin would fall off with the clay, leaving the finest barbecued chickens in the world.

Sunday afternoons Estolano and others of his gang often went to town, Running north and south almost the whole distance between the Mission and the town was a long hill. The boys would usually come to town through a deep gulch on the west side that ran almost straight to within a few yards of the settlement. The reason they took this hidden trail was to keep out of sight of the Fathers who were reputed oftentimes to play a spy glass over the country to see what they could see.

On these Sunday afternoon visits to town they always called at the home of Mrs. Caroline Jimeno Kahn for afternoon tea. Mrs. Kahn was a de la Guerra and knew all their sweethearts. She always managed to have them at her house when the boys came. After tea she would play the piano and all would dance.

Whenever a circus came to town Father O'Keefe and occasionally Father Wade would each escort a dozen or so boys who desired to go and who had the money to pay for their admission.

Most of the picnics of the Santa Barbara town people were held in a grove situated along the country road about a mile west of the Mission. One afternoon Osvaldo, Jesús and Estolano stole away to one of the town picnics. They did not go directly from the Mission, as they didn't want the people at the picnic to think that they had skipped out from school.

They went around to the north of the picnic grounds, intending to come in from the beach on the west. Near the picnic ground there was a little farm with a white board fence along the front and a big gate. The boys were just going in through the gate when a good-sized dog came tearing down the hill towards them. The dog attacked Estolano, stopping the three boys short. Estolano grabbed the dog by the nose and, although it was clawing him with his front feet, he hung on for dear life. Osvaldo in the meantime, picking up a good-sized log, dropping it on the dog's back. This stopped the battle. The animal crawled away through the fence dragging its hind legs. Its back was broken.

While the boys were getting over their scare, the ranch owner in a rage suddenly appeared with a shotgun in his hand. Fortunately for the boys, Nick Covarruvias, the Sheriff of Santa Barbara County, and a companion, while strolling out from the picnic grounds, had seen the whole performance. They hurried to the aid of the boys, ordering the man to take his gun home and stay there.

The picnic ground was not more than a hundred yards away, and the sheriff took the boys over and got them some wine to settle their nerves. All the girls crowded around, and the sheriff told them how valiantly Estolano and his companions had defended themselves from the vicious dog. Everybody at the picnic shared their lunch with them, and the three young truants had a very enjoyable afternoon.

During the summer months at the school the boys were often taken to the beaches for a swim. Sometimes they went to the town beach two miles distant. At other times they went to the Point Concepción Beach a little over four miles west of the Mission. Only the larger boys were allowed to make this trip. Generally they went in groups, each group superintended by a Prefect. Most of the boys liked best to travel with Father O'Keefe. Each group carried its own lunch, consisting of sandwiches, meat, cake and fruit. After the swim each group would repair to the shade of some large oak tree and there eat their frugal repast.

After a good rest various groups would go back down to the beach and practice foot racing, hop, skip and jump, and the running broad jump. Father Wade was the champion running jumper. Although clad in his heavy, cumbersome Franciscan habit and with sandals for shoes, nevertheless he could clear twenty-two feet. He seemed simply to fly through the air. Oftentimes he would be turned more than half way around when he landed. The rule in jumping always was to take the imprint of the heels as the person's mark. In the case of Father Wade, however, it was oftentimes the toe of his left foot that served as his mark instead of his heel. Neither Estolano nor any of the other boys could reach even the twenty-foot mark.

Chapter XXXII

HOME AGAIN

ABOUT THE TWENTITH of June each year the commencement exercises of the Franciscan College were held. The exact date depended on just what day the northbound steamer was expected. The *Orizaba* and the *Oriflame,* also the antique *Senator,* were then plying the coast waters between San Francisco and San Diego. The steamers touched at Ventura and Santa Barbara, with no other stops. Twice a week a steamer docked at Santa Barbara.

For three weeks before commencement the boys who were to take part in the dialogues and declamations were allowed to go down to the creek back of the Mission and practise their parts to their heart's content. At first the commencement exercises took place in the Carillo ampitheater, a rather dilapidated adobe structure on the edge of town at the end of State Street, then the main street of Santa Barbara. Later José Lobero, the band leader, built a large theater, the first one in Santa Barbara, which he called the Lobero. From then on the annual commencement exercises were held there.

On steamer day after commencement, all the baggage of the scholars living in Northern California was carted down to the steamship office on the wharf. After their tickets were purchased the boys had only to wait around town until the steamer arrived at the dock. Half a dozen boys, including Estolano, hired saddle horses from a livery stable and rode all over town and along the beaches. In the evening they put up their horses and went to supper at old Rufat's, a French chef who had a sort of hostelry on State Street.

The steamer came in about midnight, and all went on board. As there were no staterooms available, the boys had to occupy lounges and chairs in the cabin. Some slept while others just relaxed. About daybreak there were footsteps outside the cabin along the deck. Estolano opened the window back of his seat and looked out. Perhaps it was because of the fresh air suddenly striking his face. Anyway Estolano became a very seasick boy. Right then and there, fast and furiously, he got rid of his supper of the night before.

There were perhaps fifty or sixty school boys on board. During the forenoon a canvas was stretched out on deck and fifteen or twenty of the boys availed themselves of the opportunity to lie out flat on the deck. The whole bunch spent the day without a bite to eat. Estolano made two or three attempts to walk around the deck, but the smell from the kitchen below, or maybe it was the oil from the engine room, sent him first to the rail and then back to the canvas again.

The steward came on deck with a lot of boiled abalones. He handed them around to the sick boys. He told them to peel the abalones and chew on them. The meat of the abalone is very white. It chews like rubber, dissolves gradually and is very savory. Some of the boys tried the abalones and not only got over their seasickness but felt like they had had a good meal.

Most of the boys on the steamer were from San Francisco. There were quite a number, however, from Marysville, Santa Rosa, Weaverville, Chico, and also from Santa Cruz, Watsonville, Monterey and Castroville. When the steamer arrived in San Francisco most of the boys who lived outside of the city went to the Brooklyn Hotel on Bush Street, between Sansome and Montgomery. John Kelly, a son of the proprietor, was one of the school boys, and nearly everyone followed him to his father's hotel.

Estolano stayed in San Francisco until all his money was gone, save just enough to pay his way to San Juan. His hotel bill was unpaid. He went to Mr. Kelly and explained his predicament. He asked to leave his baggage in his room until he could go home and get the money to pay him. This was all satisfactory to Mr. Kelly.

Estolano went to San Juan. His sister Lupe was living in town then. She had sold her interest in the Ranchito and had some money on deposit with Bartolo Samit, the store keeper. Estolano told her his troubles, and she let him have forty dollars. With this he returned to San Francisco, paid his hotel bill and then had a splendid time taking in the Fourth of July celebration with its parades and band music galore.

While in the city he took in Woodward's Gardens and also visited the foundations of the new City Hall and of the Palace Hotel, which were just being started. Estolano enjoyed himself hugely. The railroad fare from San Francisco to Sargent's Station was five and a half dollars and the stage fare to San Juan a dollar more.

It was not until the fifteenth of July that Estolano reached his mother's home at Cantua, near the Black Hill on the New Idria Road. He spent a month at home, riding around the country. Three married brothers and two sisters lived almost adjoining, and every Sunday all would come home. The first thing on their arrival was to kneel before the Crucifix and say the Rosary, Estolano's mother always leading. After that all would visit throughout the day, dance and play forfeit games.

Estolano never missed an opportunity to ride over to his Uncle Justo's ranch. It was called the "Coyote" and was located up in the mountains on Coyote Creek about seven miles east of Old Gilroy. Salmon, trout, flounders and some speckled trout were plentiful in Coyote Creek, and the family caught as many fish every day as were wanted. There was plenty of game in the mountains to the northwest. The ranch consisted of a fine vineyard and orchard, horses, cattle and sheep. Six cousins lived there. Three were boys, Juan, Gusman and Oliverio, and three were girls, Soledad, Juliana and Cecelia. The latter was named after her mother and was Estolano's favorite. She was just his age. She could play the guitar nicely and was a good singer. But above all she was a good cow-girl. She had a fine side-saddle, which she used on Sundays in riding to church at a chapel near Gilroy. For every day use she had a man's saddle.

One day Oliverio, who was at least ten years older than Cecelia, led a young horse down to the creek beach to break to ride. This sandy bar consisted of two or three acres and was a good place to break a horse. The colt would soon tire out wading in the sand. The soft ground in turn was also a good place to land if a person were bucked off. Several of the family, including Cecelia and Estolano, were there on horseback to watch the show. Oliverio saddled up the pony and got on its back. About the third jump the pony landed Oliverio in the sand head first. Although Oliverio was unhurt, still he would not get on again.

Cecelia began poking fun at her brother.

"Put my saddle on the pony," she boasted, "and I'll ride him."

The boys did so. Although the pony bucked and jumped pretty lively, Cecelia stayed on and showed her brother that she could ride the horse even if he couldn't.

At the foot of a tall pine tree that grew on a hillside near the ranch was the grave of a flyer, Joaquin Castro. He was the old grandfather of the family. Out of tin and cedar wood he had made himself a set of wings which he thought were large enough and strong enough to hold up his weight. These he flapped by means of strong cords which he worked with his hands. By pulling the cords he could force the wings to open and flap, bird fashion.

After a long period of perfecting the wings the old gentleman took them up on a hill. Here he selected a tall piñion tree on a level spot of ground. He trimmed all the branches off of one side of the tree to make room for his machine. Then he climbed up some twenty feet from the ground, fastened on his wings and made a jump forward. His wings flopped all right. So did he, striking the ground with such force that he sprained his ankle, injured one arm and bruised his body. He also lost considerable skin off of his face. It took him quite a while to recover from his first flight which was also his last. Not long afterward the old inventor passed away. They buried him humbly at the base of the tree from which he had essayed to fly.

Estolano's cousin, Gusman, was a natural born genius. He no doubt inherited his ability from his air-minded grandfather. He was a good barber, harness and saddle maker, shoemaker, tailor, blacksmith, gunsmith, silversmith and machinist. He could take old boot tops and turn out a nice pair of slippers from them. He made nice dress shoes for his sisters. He was his own harness maker and was able to dress a bare saddle tree as well as any common saddle maker. He could play the guitar, flute and piccolo and also sing. He wrote a legible hand, plain, even and clear. He never attended English school, but he could talk English fairly well, and also read it. In Spanish, however, he was more than good. He composed beautiful poetry and wrote nice letters. He stood six feet high and weighed one hundred and eighty pounds. He was light complexioned with blue eyes and light brown wavy hair.

Gusman had a small apparatus in the shape of a little cart or wagon which came pretty near being perpetual motion. It had four little wheels on which to run. There was a lever of some sort to start the thing going. Around and around the room it would travel. It would keep going indefinitely unless it hit the wall or some other obstruction.

One time Gusman and Estolano wanted to go hunting. Gusman had a rim-fire Henry rifle. Unfortunately all the cartridges he had on hand at the ranch were central fire. They fitted the gun nicely but the weapon would not explode them. He took the gun apart, went into his little workshop and in a jiffy had the striking pin so fixed that it would explode both rim and central fire ammunition.

Estolano had a silver mounted head stall given him by his father, Don Manuel. It had a large oval-shaped silver plate on the frontal piece. On this Gusman worked three raised letters in gold—E. F. L.—over an inch in height and clearly discernable at a distance of fifty feet or more. He also ornamented the martingale with a large silver heart placed in the center of the leather heart. With a row of small silver buttons he also outlined the edge of the leather heart. These buttons were made of half-bit Mexican coins that Estolano had taken from the *pantalonas* made for him years before by his mother in his bull-fighting days at the Ranchito.

One day at the Coyote Ranch four of the boys saddled up and went out hunting in the hills. Juan, the oldest of the cousins, rode with Estolano. The former had a single shot rifle and the latter a Colts .45 revolver. Oliverio rode with a young French boy named Guillermino who was living at the ranch. Each of these had rifles. After traveling together several miles the party divided. The first two hunters went over the top of a big hill while Juan and Estolano took a trail skirting the foot.

Juan proposed that they dismount and follow the trail on foot. After walking about a quarter of a mile they heard three shots, Bang! Bang! Bang! Presently three big deer showed up on a rocky point, scared out by Oliverio and the French boy hunting above them. Juan fired. He missed. His gun was a muzzle loader and had only one shot. Suddenly, while he was reloading, three more deer came running down the trail. Estolano was so taken by surprise at the appearance of six deer all at one time that he hardly knew which one to shoot at first. Without taking definite aim he began firing at random. All his bullets he soon saw were cutting the leaves above the animals' backs.

There was a rock in the trail over which the deer, running single file, were jumping. As the last one, high in the air was leaping over the rock, Estolano, this time taking definite aim, fired. The deer fell, but instantly picking itself up again, kept on running down the hill. Hurrying along on foot the two boys about a hundred and fifty yards from where the fray had taken place, found Estolano's deer. It was a big black-tailed buck and was already dead. They dressed it then and there. Going back for their horses they slung it across Estolano's mount for it was his game. He walked ahead leading his horse while Juan rode along behind.

Before they got to the foot of the hill Juan suddenly hollered: "Whoa!"

Both stopped. Still farther down below them perhaps a hundred yards they could see a deer's head quite plainly. Juan shot at it from horseback. Instantly another deer jumped up. Juan, feverishly reloading his gun, fired a second time.

To Estolano's amazement when the boys reached the bottom of the hill there lay TWO dead deer!

Juan and Estolano both walked the rest of the way back to the house some four or five miles. They were feeling quite proud of the three fine bucks slung across their saddle horses. Later in the day Oliverio and Guillermino returned. They had had no luck at all. Every deer that they had shot at they had missed.

"We got three of your deer you sent us," declared Juan tauntingly as he pointed proudly to the three deer hanging on the limb of a tree in the back yard.

All that Oliverio and the French boy had to show for their day's hunting was a fresh bear skin!

It was time for Estolano to be returning to college. His uncle Justo was well acquainted with Father Gonzales at the Santa Barbara Mission. He asked Estolano to do him a favor. He wanted him to go to Father Gonzales and ask him for one of his old Franciscan habits. Estolano promised to do so and said that he would bring it with him the next time he came home from college. Justo was a tall, slim, dignified old man, and he wanted the Franciscan habit for his shroud!

Chapter XXXIII

UNDER ARREST

DURING ESTOLANO'S second year at college there came to the Mission a middle-aged Spanish Californian who wanted to become a Franciscan Brother. He was a little off mentally. Father Gonzales, the Superior, had known the man's father, and so he was allowed to stay at the Mission and was given free board and lodging. He wore no habit. The boys called him by his Christian name, Don José. Sometimes in the evenings he would wander over among the boys in the play yard and tell them of his early adventures.

"I once went to visit my uncle," he told them. "My uncle lived in a little cabin up on the high hills. He was taking care of cattle and I stayed over night with him. Early the next morning I got up and looking out of the window, saw a deer grazing about forty yards away. I grabbed my uncle's rifle, a muzzle-loader, and started in loading in order to shoot the deer. When I came to put in the bullet I found there were none. I asked my uncle where I could find some and he said there wasn't any. In looking around for bullets I had come upon a twenty penny cut spike. It just fitted into the muzzle of the gun. So I put the spike down the barrel thinking I would have a little fun anyway. I stepped around the corner of the cabin all ready to shoot. Just then the deer lifted up its hind foot and started scratching its ear. I took deliberate aim, let fly, and hit the mark. There stood the deer with its hind foot nailed to the side of its head!"

Many changes had been made in and around the school during the summer vacation. In the upper story of the Monastery at the west end a new study hall had been completed. The new hall was much brighter and more commodious than the former one, which had now been turned into a music room and recreation hall. A new trunk room had been provided for the boys. Also a row of single rooms had been partitioned off and were available to boys who could afford to pay five dollars a month extra for the privilege of having a room to themselves. Estolano quickly signed up for one of these as it gave him more freedom. Those occupying private rooms were not required to go to the study hall to do their studying.

A water system had been installed during the summer months. Also a wash room had been built with a line of wash basins on the four sides of the room. Running water with faucets had been piped to each wash dish. This water system was quite an improvement over that of the previous year when poor old Brother David, with a Chinese yoke and two five-gallon oil cans, had carried the water for the boys from a reservoir a quarter of a mile distant. Several barrels placed along the side walls of the long corridor had to be kept full at all times. Poor old Brother David was on the go constantly. He could be seen at all times of the day forever counting his Rosary beads with bowed head as he traveled back and forth carrying water. He seldom looked up or spoke to anyone.

Boys who had rooms of their own did their own chamber work. But there was a Brother named Reid who made up the beds in the dormitories. Brother Reid was about six feet four inches tall and very spare, just as his name implied. He suffered from a nervous affliction. If he happened not to see or hear a person coming into the room where he was working and they hailed him: "Hi, Brother Reid!" he would jump heavenward and nearly hit the ceiling. The boys enjoyed teasing him. Whenever they could take him unawares, they would yell at him just to see him jump.

Estolano found school much more interesting this second year. He had a number of new studies and was kept pretty busy. He took among other subjects Natural Philosophy, Astronomy, rhetoric, commercial arithmetic and book-keeping. Besides these he had Spanish and French.

Estolano also decided to take up piano lessons. Father O'Keefe was the teacher. The practice piano was in the large room at the entrance to the church choir. Instead of practicing, he would spend much of his time trying to pick out tunes with one finger. Father O'Keefe caught him at it several times and reprimanded him for it. Finally one day when he heard Estolano still persisting in this one finger practice, he came up and summarily dismissed him. He advised him to go to Brother John, who was now the violin teacher, and take violin instead of piano.

Brother John taught both flute and violin. Estolano had his own ideas and thought that he would rather learn to play the flute. Brother John produced a flute and Estolano had his first lesson. This was to fix his lips properly over the apperture, blow against it and produce a sound. But Estolano soon quit the flute, for after three lessons he still could not get a single note from the reed. Estolano next bought a violin and started in taking lessons. He could get some sort of sound out of the violin right from the start. It was pretty discordant, it is true, but it was not long before he could mete out "Wearing of the Green," Yankee Doodle," and other popular airs of the time.

A large telescope had been installed in one of the church towers, and once or twice a week the astronomy teacher would take Estolano and the other boys up in the tower to view the heavenly wonders. Jupiter with its many moons and Saturn with its rings were generally the planets sought out.

On Thursdays the college boys would often go out on the flat west of the Mission and play baseball. Father O'Keefe and Father Wade were both good ball players and were often chosen to play along with the boys. On Sundays the College sometimes played in town against the Santa Barbara College Club, a Protestant organization, and at other times with the new town club. On these occasions the ball grounds, situated on the outskirts of the town, were crowded with town people. This fact would pep up the Mission boys to play their best.

Estolano usually played shortstop. He was also a good runner. On one occasion when playing with the town club the Mission boys after their ninth inning were only two tallies ahead. A Los Angeles young man, named Leslie, who was employed in a blacksmith shop, hit a straight fly, and it was coming directly at Estolano. The ball was too high over Estolano's head for him to catch it, and so he ran on a line with it for about twenty yards. He leaped into the air and caught it as it was passing over his head. He held the ball high in the air, and the batter was called out by the umpire. This put a feather in Estolano's cap, and after that, so long as he remained in Santa Barbara, his position on the team was secure.

When Comencement time came the Lobero Theater which was under construction near the de la Guerra Square, was sufficiently finished to permit the holding of the college exercises there. Estolano was in a play taking the part of a doctor, while Gaspar de la Guerra took the part of the patient. In the play Gaspar's malady was diagnosed as simply laziness. Estolano sent to San Juan for his father's gold headed cane to use in the play. Gaspar stuffed a feather pillow under his clothes, but the audience did not know this. When the young doctor proceeded right then and there to administer his medicine by lashing the patient with his cane the spectators howled with merriment.

Commencement over, a large number of the college boys again sailed away on the steamer for Northern California. In

San Francisco in those days the sidewalks were made out of wood. There were wide cracks between the planks. As Estolano walked down Fourth Street on his way to the Townsend Street Depot, he was jauntily swinging his father's old cane that he was taking back home with him. How nice to be a doctor in real life he thought to himself and go walking down the street with a gold headed cane, meriting the respect and esteem of everyone.

Don Manuel's was a sword cane. As Estolano sauntered along he accidentally ran the end of it down between the planks. Without his noticing it, the cane came apart, the sword, about two feet long, remaining in his hand while the rest of the stick stood sticking up in the crack. Estolano had gone about fifteen or twenty steps. When he realized his loss he started back to recover the stick.

A policeman had picked up the end of the cane and was walking fast to catch up with Estolano.

"Young fellow, I place you under arrest!"

Estolano was startled.

"That's a sword cane you are carrying," declared the policeman. "They are against the law. They are concealed weapons."

"It's only an heirloom," protested Estolano. "My great-grandfather brought it over from Spain in 1776 when he settled in Mexico."

"Heirloom or no heirloom makes no difference," howled the policeman authoritatively. "However I will let you go this time. But don't let me catch you around here again with it."

The policeman handed Estolano the cane, and the humbled little doctor made his way thoughtfully to the Southern Pacific train.

"I guess I'm not so important here in San Francisco as I am in college!"

View from the Old Bell Tower, 1947
John Howell Photo

Chapter XXXIV

STAMPEDING

ESTOLANO'S BROTHER, Gracia, came up Tres Pinos way looking for vaqueros to help him drive a band of cattle from Soledad to Millbrae, near San Francisco. He was employed by a Mr. Dumphy, a San Francisco wholesale butcher. Gracia wanted to hire six men. He said that he paid two dollars and a half per day and "grub" if he furnished the mounts, or three dollars and a half if the rider furnished his own horse. Estolano promptly asked his brother to hire him as one of the vaqueros and he agreed. Gracia also employed Antonio Herrera and Felipe German. That was now three that he had. Since Estolano was going, he said that he would take his son, José, Estolano's nephew, to keep him company. José and Estolano were about the same age. Gracia also took Mariano Soto, another nephew, and one of his own ranch hands, José Gutierrez. That completed the outfit. All were to meet at Gracia's ranch just north of San Juan Bautista.

An early start was made from San Juan, and the seven arrived in Soledad in the evening. There they met the cattle they were to drive to Millbrae. At Soledad there were large fields and corrals and the cattle were kept in these over night. Early the next morning the herd boss and Gracia made the count. Gracia receipted for three hundred and fifteen head. The cowboys who had delivered the cattle at Soledad helped to get the band across the Salinas River. The water was quite low, but the stream was treacherous. There is quicksand all through it. The men had to be extra careful to keep the cattle on just a certain crossing which was free from the treacherous quicksands. They got through without mishap.

After leaving the river, Gracia placed Estolano and José on the lead. Then one man on either side along the center. The remaining three drove from behind.

They had gone about ten miles from the river when they came to a long picket fence that followed the road for some distance. Gracia decided it would be a good camping place for the night. While Estolano and José held the cattle along side of the fence, the others built a fire and made coffee. After all had eaten their supper of coffee and bread, three were detailed to stand guard until eleven. Then another set were to take their places while the first three took a nap. Estolano and José were in the first detail. They kept together most of the time letting their horses snooze while they sat at ease in their saddles and talked.

It was now getting almost dark. The two boys were beginning to get lonesome. They rolled their cigarettes, and Estolano struck a match. After lighting the two cigarettes Estolano was seized with the crazy notion of touching the match to a big bunch of Spanish moss hanging over his head. Unexpectedly this flared up strong. That was what started the stampede!

The two or three beeves standing along side of the fence let out a bellow. In a jiffy the whole band was up and running full speed back towards the river. Estolano and José rode ahead trying to stop the mad rush but to no avail. Gracia and the rest of the men rode right into the band trying to head off the cattle. They raced right along side of the leaders of the stampede. They pounded them with their lariats and urged their horses time after time against the sides the cattle. Gradually the seven riders turned the direction of the charging herd and finally had them running north back towards the old camp ground. By the time they had them back in camp again the cattle had run at least five miles.

"Estolano, I thought you were a better cattleman than that!" That was all that Gracia said, but it cut his little brother's pride to the quick.

Gracia decided to keep the cattle moving. There would be no more camping that night. At Natividad about six miles farther ahead there was a fenced lane. Here he decided to hold the cattle. When within about two miles of the Natividad Hotel, he sent Estolano and José ahead to order breakfast for all. Estolano and José were to eat their breakfast and be ready to guard the cattle when they arrived in the lane while the rest of the vaqueros went on to breakfast.

By the time the cattle had reached Stokes' Ranch after leaving Natividad, it was the middle of the day and the weather was very hot. There was lots of green grass there and nice shady live oaks. Gracia let the cattle remain there until late in the afternoon. It was rather monotonous to Estolano watching the cattle eat and snooze. Most of the men lay down in the shade and took it easy. Estolano had two dime novels with him. He could translate the English of these right along into Spanish as though they had been written in that language. He translated aloud and José listened most attentively. In that way the two boys got through the long day.

Supper was eaten at the Joaquin Soto's ranch on the south end of the Carneros Grant. At daybreak everyone was up and ready to travel. The men circled the hills around the wagon road, and Gracia had a chance to look the cattle over. He discovered a shortage. When they got to Transito Rojas' Ranch at the edge of the Carneros just west of San Juan he sent three men back to look for the missing cattle. The rest of the men were to wait where they were, there being good feed for the stock. About ten o'clock the men were back with thirty head of steers. Then the men had breakfast at Rojas' Ranch. The band reached Gracia's ranch beyond San Juan about two o'clock in the afternoon. Gracia had a good field all under fence. The cattle were driven in and counted. The count tallied all right. The party remained at Gracia's ranch all that day and night, where the men as well as the horses and cattle had a good rest and plenty to eat all around.

The next morning at daybreak all were on their way. By noon they were on the outskirts of Gilroy. There they held the cattle and had dinner at a ranch house along the road. Later that evening they made the Twenty-one Mile House on the road to San Jose. Here there was a good hotel and a splendid fenced field where no herding was necessary. However four men did guard duty that night. Gracia, Estolano and José had fine beds in the hotel. All the next day and night were spent at the Twenty-one Mile House, after which the band went forward once more.

No more trouble was experienced until the band reached the Don Segundo Roble's Ranch. This was a few miles south of Mayfield. Here they were to rest and pasture the cattle for another couple of days. Don Segundo had a good field and pasture, but there was not sufficient water for so many cattle. It was necessary every day to drive the cattle out to the highway and take them about a mile north to a large creek that flowed beside the road. Twice while they were there they drove the cattle to water. This was about two o'clock in the afternoon each day.

Returning from the water the second afternoon, Estolano and José were driving behind. A troublesome old brindled stag was lagging behind. This so exasperated Estolano that he would ride his horse right up against the steer, slip his foot out of the stirrup and give him a dig on his rump with his spur. Estolano's spurs were small but sharp. After a good dig Mr. Stag would speed up for a time.

On this particular afternoon this stag kept lazying along, and Estolano got after him good and plenty. Estolano must have dug him pretty hard the last time for the stag threw up his tail and started on the run. To Estolano's terror his spur had caught fast in the steer's tail. The stag was dragging Estolano, still on his horse, right along. Soon they were all in the midst of the herd. Had not Estolano's horse been a good cowpony Estolano would have been dragged from his saddle. All that saved him from being trampled to death was that the pony knew just what to do. He kept right up with the steer.

Estolano was wearing made-to-order boots that fitted him rather snug. His foot was half out of the boot, due to the stag's hard pulling. Estolano leaned forward and with his hand managed to get the boot the rest of the way off. Away went the stag with Estolano's boot dangling from his tail. It was quite a while before the boot and spur dropped off and fell to the ground where Estolano recovered them. In the meantime the men on ahead were having a hard time holding the cattle back and preventing them from again stampeding.

It took twelve days to drive the cattle from Soledad to Millbrae. On the return trip the outfit reached San Jose late in the evening. Here everybody was paid off. The next morning Estolano rode through Old Gilroy and the Soap Lake District direct to Tres Pinos where he was soon again with his mother, settled as he thought for the summer.

The Rancho Tallow Kettle

Lupe Anzar and Wife

Chapter XXXV

THE WILLOW TREE

ESTOLANO no longer had any stock of any kind. His two saddle horses, including Tunante, his mother had sold nearly a year before to Francisco and Joaquin Barcelon. The horses were now in Sonora. The Barcelons had ridden them back to Hermosillo, their old home in Mexico.

Ignacio Gomez, a Tres Pinos neighbor, had a number of pretty saddle horses. When he found that Estolano had no saddle horse of any kind he drove his *compomario* into his corral and insisted that Estolano should take his choice of the lot.

"I want to give you one of my horses to ride for the summer," he told Estolano.

Estolano however refused to make a choice, and so Ignacio picked out one for him, a medium-sized horse, gray roan in color, high lifed and as active as a kitten. A person could ride this horse up in front of a four-foot rail fence, simply cluck to him, move the reins forward the least bit and the horse would clear the fence in a single leap.

"Tomorrow there is going to be a big barbecue and dance at El Sauce," mentioned Ignacio casually.

The Cortez family had lost their Grant near San Juan Bautista and had moved to the Panoche Valley. They called their new ranch El Sauce, meaning the "Willow Tree." Estolano, who knew the family well, needed no special encouragement to attend.

The fiesta was a big success. Besides the many people living in the neighborhood, there were present the Hernandez family together with the Vargas and Gomez families who had many grown-up girls. There was plenty to eat and drink. In the evening there was dancing. The music was fine and Estolano found plenty of señoritas to dance with. After the dance a fine supper was served.

The Cortez children consisted of two grown-up girls, Clara, eighteen, a brunette, tall, slender and quite pretty; Caroline, the next girl, was about sixteen years old, very fair and plump and not nearly so tall as Clara. There were also three boys ranging in age from ten to fourteen. Doña Juana was the children's grandmother. Although Estolano liked Clara he liked Caroline much better.

At the fiesta Doña Juana asked Estolano if he would be willing to accept the position of teacher at the ranch. She offered him board, room, washing and thirty dollars a month. Estolano simply jumped at the chance, both to earn money and at the same time try out his hand at teaching school.

As soon as arrangements could be made Estolano began his teaching. Near the adobe house where the Cortez family lived there was a long, low timber building with three or four good rooms. One was especially adapted for school purposes. This was promptly fixed up in tip-top shape. Seats were provided for the pupils and a nice office chair and table for the teacher.

The children had plenty of Spanish books but none in English. Estolano was to teach them both languages. He made out a little order for books and other stationery which Tomás, the foreman of the ranch, promptly ordered from Hollister. The school started with the Spanish books, but in a few days the whole of the school supplies arrived. There were pens, ink, pen holders, Spencerian copy books, a small blackboard, chalk, slates and pencils. Among the books were half a dozen English primers.

Everything was running very smoothly. Estolano had started the children all in one class. He would give them the first line in their English primer and then write it for them on the blackboard along with the translation in Spanish. Clara was very bright and learned quickly. Caroline, however, required more explanations. But she was persistent and studied hard. When the dinner bell sounded Clara, who seemed always to have a good appetite, would rush out of the room. The boys would follow her. But not so Caroline. She would remain behind and ask for more instruction which Estolano would gladly give her.

Things were going splendidly. Estolano's pupils were progressing rapidly, both in Spanish reading and in learning the sounds of the English words in the primer. He impressed on them the duty of exchanging salutations and taught them "Good morning." "Good afternoon," and "Good evening." They also learned such short sentences as "Please give me a drink of water," "Hand me your book," "You may have a short recess now." Also the names of victuals at the table and "Please help me to some meat," or "Please pass the bread."

The children as well as the old folks were all pleased with Estolano and his school. One day at the dinner hour, however, when the children had been dismissed and Caroline was holding back as usual, her mother unfortunately happened to be near the building cutting flowers for the table. Hearing talking going on in the school room, she stepped inside to investigate. Estolano was holding Caroline on his lap. Señora Cortez merely asked Estolano why he was not at dinner.

"I was just helping Caroline," he replied, "over her difficulties with her lessons."

"Yes, I understand," said Caroline's mother, with a knowing look and walked out, leaving two very embarrassed young people.

School continued that afternoon as though nothing had happened. Late in the evening, however, Tomás came to Estolano's room and told him that the women of the ranch thought it best for him to resign. Although he had been there only a little more than two weeks Tomás handed Estolano a full month's pay and insisted that he take it.

The next morning the young school teacher saddled up his horse and set out for home. Estolano was growing both in stature and in experience. Bitterly he reflected, as his horse picked his way along the mountain road. The disgrace of being fired humiliated him exceedingly. But he realized that he had brought all his troubles on himself.

"Never," he resolved firmly as his mother's house came into view, "will I ever mix love and duty again!"

Chapter XXXVI

ESTOLANO'S CURIOSITY

ESTOLANO SADDLED up his horse one Sunday afternoon and struck out to visit his nephew, Bernardo, who was herding sheep that summer for Estanislao Hernandez in the Quien Sabe Valley. Bernardo was supposed to be camped about fifteen miles away at an old adobe in the northern end of the valley. Estolano had never been there. At the Hernandez place, called Buena Vista. Estolano inquired and was told that he had three miles farther to go. He was directed to follow along the foothills on the west side and he would come to the old Quien Sabe ranch house.

It was already dusk, and before he had gone half way it was entirely dark. He kept following the foothills but there were so many ravines around which he had to travel that time was taken up wholesale, and he seemed to be getting nowhere. As it was now dark, he decided that it was best to make camp for the night and wait for daylight. He got off his horse, unsaddled and tied it to a tree where it could have all the oat hay it wanted to eat. Estolano piled up a big mound of hay for himself and fixed up a bed, using his saddle for a pillow.

Though it was now July and only the middle of summer, the night was cold. Estolano had his cloak with him and a good clean saddle blanket. With these he made himself as comfortable as possible, composing himself for a good snooze.

He had hardly relaxed when the howl of a coyote reverberated through the valley. Another and another howl followed until they made the lonely night horrifying. A horned owl flew by and perched on a nearby tree. Soon he began his "To Who, Hoo, Hoo." Among the old Spaniards the owl was supposed to be the devil's own bird. The cold chills ran through Estolano. "To Who, Hoo, Hoo." Finally jumping up in desperation he fired his revolver in the direction of the owl. Then he fired two more shots toward the hillside where he thought the howls of the coyote came from. This had a good effect. The owl flew away and the coyote became silent.

Estolano laid down in the dark, but all desire for sleep had been scared out of him. He never slept a wink all night. He was nervous and couldn't compose himself. In the far distance soon he heard the coyote again. Sometimes it sounded as though there were a dozen of them. The night dragged on. He just laid there on the hay wishing and waiting for daylight to come. When the first rays of dawn finally appeared, he saddled up his horse and proceeded on his way. Not two hundred feet away from where he had spent the night, on rounding a hill he came upon an adobe house hidden away like a timid animal!

Estolano was both astonished and disgusted. Here he had spent the most miserable night of his life, and all the while only two hundred feet from a house. He hollered and presently he could hear someone stirring within. A drowsy young man made his appearance at the door. It was Bernardo! The towsle-headed youth was certainly astonished to see anyone approaching at that early hour, but his delight on discovering it was Estolano woke him up thoroughly.

"Come right in, Tio. How in the world did you manage to get here so early in the morning?"

"I came last night. But you had gone to bed and I didn't want to disturb you. I slept out in the hay."

"But you shouldn't have done that," protested Bernardo.

Then Estolano told him the truth and they both had a good laugh.

Bernardo immediately busied himself getting a fire started in the dilapidated old cook stove that served as part of his camp equipment. He broke half a dozen eggs in a frying pan of sizzling grease into which a few strips of bacon had already been thrown. The aroma was irresistible. Estolano had had nothing to eat since noon the day before. The fried eggs together with coffee and cold tortillas that Bernardo served up composed such a breakfast that Estolano fairly dived in head-first and with both feet. He was so desperately hungry and Bernardo's breakfast tasted so good. With one gulp he swallowed nearly half a cup of coffee at a time.

"Bernardo," declared the half choking Estolano, "you are wasting your time here herding sheep. You ought to go to town and start a restaurant."

"I can see plainly," bantered the young cook, "that I would go broke in no time if all my customers ate the way you do."

Estolano suppressed a smile, as he continued to swallow whole mouthfuls of Bernardo's wonderful cooking.

Bernardo looked on in amusement. "Don't they feed you anything at your school?"

"Not such a breakfast as this," truthfully replied Estolano.

Shoving back from the table Estolano looked admiringly at his nephew.

"Do you remember the time you and I ran away from the Ranchito on old Tom and walked the eighteen miles to the Cantua?"

"Do I!' laughed Bernardo. "I haven't walked eighteen miles since in one day and I hope I never have to. Weren't we tired and sore the next morning?"

"And have you seen any more ghosts lately?" chuckled Estolano. "I sure thought Dolores was never going to get you calmed down. And I never ran so fast in my life, either," declared Bernardo's partner in the escapade.

Becoming more sober in his remarks Estolano asked: 'What are you doing now?"

"I've got a good job with Hernandez herding sheep," replied Bernardo. With sheep subconsciously on his mind, Bernardo glanced critically out the window at the thousand head of sheep making their way up the hill, grazing slowly farther afield in the early morning light.

"You must find it terribly lonesome," said Estolano thoughtfully.

"It wouldn't be so bad if I liked to read."

"Don't you like to read?" asked the college man in surprise.

"It's just such a life as you ought to lead, Estolano. All the time in the world to read. Practically nothing to do but lie around from daylight until dark."

"I like to read all right," replied Estolano. "But I wouldn't want to be tied down all the time. If there was going to be a fiesta somewhere, I would simply forget all about the sheep and go."

"Then you wouldn't last long with Hernandez. You can lie around all day in camp and do nothing, and he don't care. But just you leave them for one night and he would be after you good and plenty. Besides Hernandez would see to it that you didn't have a horse in camp. You couldn't get away even if you wanted to."

Estolano didn't tell his nephew that he had once herded sheep for this same Hernandez and on horseback, too.

Leaving the dishes still sitting on the table where they had eaten out of them, the two boys started out the door together to look around.

"But I like it, Estolano. If I just had the money to buy a band of sheep of my own! But I don't suppose I ever will have. It costs money to buy sheep. I gamble a little. Maybe I'll make a big killing someday. But," reflected Bernardo seriously, "the man who puts his money in sheep always becomes well off."

Estolano looked over the band of sheep carefully. He could see that Bernardo was giving them the best of care.

"By the way, Estolano. You've got lots of money. Why don't you buy me a band of sheep? I'll herd them and we'll divide the profits. You can live in town somewhere and take life easy. I'll do the work and run the business. You'll make money and I'll make money. Eventually I'll become a rich man like yourself. All I need is a start."

"I'll think about it, Bernardo. Maybe when I'm out of school we can make some such deal as that."

Leaving Bernardo in a happy mood, Estolano set out late that afternoon for home. When he got to the house a little before dark, he found his mother sitting on the front porch sewing. Not long after they both heard someone in the creek beside the house. Both were startled. The creek was wide and lined on either side with brush. The sound of a horse's feet could be heard coming down the stony bed. They wondered why anyone would be traveling along the creek bed instead of following the county road.

Presently a little man on a large dark gray horse emerged and rode cautiously up to the house. He stopped without dismounting. The man was well armed.

"Good evening," he said, ingratiatingly.

Estolano and his mother both answered uneasily: "Good evening, sir."

"I am very hungry," said the stranger. "Could I get a bite to eat?"

Estolano's mother never turned a hungry person away from her door.

"Dismount and come in," she said.

The stranger rode around back of the house out of sight where there was a large live oak tree and tied his horse. Then he came in the house and waited while supper was being prepared.

Estolano had been reading *Paul and Virginia* in Spanish and the book lay on a chair near where he and the stranger sat. Estolano had read the same story in French at college. There was one part that Estolano thought very pathetic and touching. He had marked the place in the Spanish text. The stranger picked up the book and happened to turn to this passage. After reading for a while he put the book down. Estolano noticed two big tears rolling down his cheeks.

After the man had eaten his supper he came back into the living room.

"I have to keep hidden," he confided to Estolano and his mother and he showed them where he had been wounded. "The officers are after me. An officer in Santa Cruz tried to arrest me. I considered myself innocent of any crime and I resisted him. He took a shot at me. The bullet struck me above the collar bone and bored through my left shoulder. I returned the shot and downed the officer. Being on horseback at the time, I got away."

Estolano and his mother exchanged glances with each other.

"Aren't you the outlaw, Tiburcio Vasquez?"

"That's what my mamma always call me," smiled the little man smugly.

The outlaw was wearing a large red handkerchief wound around his neck.

Estolano had never seen a bullet wound.

"Would you be willing," asked Estolano eagerly, "to let me see your wound?"

"Oh, you needn't doubt me, young man," said the outlaw removing his handkerchief. Estolano paid no attention to the man's remarks. He was interested only in examining the man's neck. Sure enough there was a place where the bullet had entered. There was a slight depression in the flesh. The wound had healed but the skin was not yet dry. Estolano helped Vasquez replace the bandage.

Chapter XXXVII

VENTURITA

ESTOLANO WAS ALWAYS interested in people. He still liked everyone. Everywhere he went his friendliness made him well received. And nearly everywhere he visited he fell in love, or thought he did, with some new girl.

This year, instead of taking the steamer to San Francisco, Estolano was to spend the summer vacation with his chum. Osvaldo de la Guerra, at the Tapo Ranch. This part of the Simi Grant belonged to the de la Guerra family. Osvaldo's older brother, Santiago, was the mayordomo, and the two boys were to leave with him in a spring wagon for the ranch early in the week following commencement.

Osvaldo and Estolano were the closest of friends. Estolano looked upon Osvaldo with the greatest admiration. Osvaldo had great powers of imagination. He was a natural-born story teller. It was customary after supper at the evening recess during term time for eight or ten of the boys to gather around Osvaldo in the school yard, and he would tell them stories. They were his own creations. His stories were much more thrilling and interesting, so the boys claimed, than any novels they had ever read. His romances were usually about Spanish Knights and their adventures.

Once he told the story of a knight who found a tunnel in the side of a mountain and being brave, the knight went in, sword in hand, to explore it. Creeping cautiously along the side of the dark, watery tunnel he suddenly put his hand on a large, hairy, slimy foot! The story that followed was so creepy that it tormented Estolano's mind for many a day.

Osvaldo, the year before, had written a play in verse called "The Rivals." It was in Spanish and had gone over splendidly. This commencement the "Rivals" was followed by another dialogue, also in verse, entitled "The Death of the Two Rivals." The two parts were to be taken by Estolano and Osvaldo himself. Their rehearsing, along with their other duties, gave them more than enough to do the last days of the school year.

The week following commencement Santiago and the two boys were off for the Tapo Ranch. The first part of the journey they traveled along the ocean shore. At Rock Point, instead of leaving the beach and going over the hill, it was possible for a team and wagon, when the tide was low, to pass safely along the shore between the cliffs and the breakers. The dangerous stretch of road extended about a mile. The tide was already coming in when Santiago arrived at Rock Point. Still there was time, he thought, to go through safely.

As the light spring wagon sped along down the beach the big waves of the sea began to roll faster and faster and higher and higher. It was a question of only a few minutes until the waves would be breaking against the cliff itself. Santiago whipped up the horses. Estolano, sitting there humped up on the seat, would far rather have been riding some bucking bronco. He then would have had some chance of exercising his skill and extricating himself from his trouble. Sitting there tamely in the wagon was not according to his nature. He had no stomach for being at the mercy of the sea over which he had no control. Just as they were about safely through, a big roller struck the wagon with a swish and a bang. Water splashed over everyone. All but Estolano laughed and thought it great fun. As it was all got soaking wet. Fortunately the weather was hot, and the boys were all dry by the time they reached the Santa Clara Hotel in Ventura.

Santiago's fiancee lived in the little Mission town, and he determined to remain over night at the hotel. After supper he quickly disappeared, leaving the boys to their own devices. Osvaldo and Estolano began wandering around the streets. About two blocks from the hotel they noticed a crowd of men going into a saloon. The two boys crowded in with the rest.

Two men were leaning up against the bar drinking whisky. Estolano quickly learned that there was a fifty dollar bet up as to which man could stand at the bar and drink whisky the longer. The contest had been going on for some time. For a full hour after the boys came in the drinking continued. About every five minutes the two men would each drink a small glass of whisky.

One of the men was medium-sized, rather spare and weighed probably not more than a hundred and thirty-five pounds. Both were young. The older man was tall and massive. He weighed nearly two hundred pounds. The large man was bombastic, talking and laughing all the time. He was ridiculing the other chap and looking down on him as much as to say: "You poor sap. You won't last much longer."

Every little while the small man would step out the door, then presently come back and take his glass quietly along with the other fellow. Estolano was more curious than the rest. He wanted to know what the little fellow was doing outside and he followed him. The little man had a small bottle in his hand and was taking a small dose apparently of some kind of medicine. Immediately up came the whisky he had just drank. The man returned to the bar room and called again for the drinks. The big man had hardly downed his glass when he began to stagger. He seized hold of the bar with both hands. His head sank to his chest. With a crash he fell to the floor dead drunk.

The little man laughed heartily and immediately called again for the drinks. He swallowed his but the man on the floor remained dead to the world. The little man pocketed his hard earned fifty dollars and walked out of the saloon. Only he and Estolano knew the secret of his keeping sober.

Osvaldo claimed that he was acquainted with some girls in Ventura, and he asked Estolano if he wouldn't like to go to their home and meet them. Estolano was only too willing. Arriving at the house, they found the two boys and the three girls of the family. Their mother was dead. Their father, Don José, was an old-time Spaniard. Manuel and José were the boys, about ten and twelve. The girls were Amanda, Adelia and Venturita. The oldest was about twenty, the others eighteen and sixteen. Adelia was a brunette with very pretty features. But it was Venturita, the youngest, who interested Estolano. She was not only gracious and beautiful, but well accomplished. She could play the piano and guitar and sang an angelic soprano. She entertained the boys with her music and sang for fully an hour. Among her selections was "La Golondrina." It was the first time Estolano had ever heard it. She also sang "Atala," a beautiful love ditty full of ardent passion. She finished by singing "La Paloma," rather ancient, but ever a favorite with Estolano. The young boys were simply captivated with the singer and her songs.

The following morning Santiago and the boys were off to an early start, as usual, for the Tapo Ranch, still some sixty miles distant. It was ten o'clock that night when they reached the ranch, but the cook got out of bed and served them a splendid supper.

The Tapo Ranch house was a one-story adobe, facing the east. The building was about forty feet long and thirty feet in width. There was the usual *sala* or living room, about sixteen feet by twenty-four. Adjoining it was a bedroom about fourteen feet square. There were three more rooms back of these two, a dining room, kitchen and another bedroom. A shed along the whole length of the building on the back was used as a store room. Along the front of the house was a large porch. At each end a bedroom had been partitioned off. The open space between was used as an outdoor dining room during the summer months.

At a nearby spring a nice little reservoir about ten feet in diameter was kept full of water, which was piped to the house. Two large walnut trees grew beside the reservoir. The trickle of the water falling into the basin from the end of the pipe bringing it from the spring could be heard all day long and all through the night. It was delightfully soothing and induced sleep with its lullaby.

An orchard all under fence occupied about ten acres near the house. There were figs, peaches, pears, plums, almonds and walnuts. There were also lots of olives and a few pomegranates. All kinds of vegetables were raised in the garden. Although cattle raising was the principal business of the ranch, there was a good-sized vineyard.

The ranch was all hills, save for the little tract of land where the orchard, vineyard and the ranch buildings were located. The cattle were pastured along the hills and on the flat near the mouth of the creek. There was also a small band of sheep with a herder who had his camp up in the hills. Incidentally, there was a bell mare with quite a bunch of good saddle horses.

In the evenings Estolano and Osvaldo would take a shotgun and go after quail and cottontails which were very plentiful. Sometimes they would bring home a large jackrabbit. The cook, who claimed that he had worked in a French hotel in Hermosillo, Mexico, and had learned cooking there, would cut the rabbit's throat and then hang it up by the hind feet until the next day. For dinner he would cook it in what he called French style, and the hungry boys could not praise his cooking enough.

Osvaldo and Estolano decided to visit the San Fernando Mission where the family of Don Andreas Pico lived. The old Mission was about thirty miles southeast of Tapo Ranch and an equal distance north of Los Angeles. The boys started early in the morning and after reaching the Simi Valley traveled along the stage road. They crossed over the San Marcos Mountain and then down into the San Fernando Valley. For miles before reaching San Fernando, the white walls of the old Mission could be seen glistening in the sunlight.

The Mission lay between the stage road and the foot hills. Estolano was riding the favorite saddle horse of Don José Antonio de la Guerra which was kept at the Tapo Ranch. The horse's name was "Traga Liguas," meaning "League Swallower." It was light brown and very powerful. This horse was supposed to be unbeatable in a ten mile race.

The boys started racing their horses in the direction of the Mission. They must have run at least five miles across the plains. Estolano was ahead all the time, although holding in his horse all he could. Finally he slowed up and waited for Osvaldo to catch up. He was afraid that such a long run would be too much for the other horse. From then on the boys took it more slowly. Don Andreas himself greeted them on their arrival at the Mission and congratulated them on their being just in time for the *merienda,* or mid-day meal.

Dinner was served in the old reception room of the Mission. The west end of the Mission buildings and corridors had all gone to ruin except about one hundred feet which was still standing and in good repair. This was neatly whitewashed and was very roomy. Here Don Andreas and his family lived. Don Andreas had many Indian servants. There were two girls and a middle-aged woman who worked in the house. The two Indian girls waited on table. The dinner consisted of rice, cooked Spanish style, roast beef, beans and potatoes, with tortillas for bread. There was no butter. Both coffee and wine were served.

The old Mission church was in ruins. A part that still had a roof on it was used for a slaughter house. At the time Estolano was there a sheep was being butchered and dressed in what had once been the chancel. Part of the graveyard walls were still doing service. The gaps had been closed by Don Andreas to keep the stock out. Prickly pears grew in the place in great profusion. Some of the head boards were still standing and the inscriptions were partly legible.

Don Andreas was the younger brother of Don Pio Pico, who had been the last Mexican Governor of California. Don Andreas was a tall, fine looking man. He wore a large gray mustache. This made him look almost fierce, but in reality he was very gentle and affable. He was a good friend of the de la Guerra family and had also known Estolano's father, Don Manuel. Don Andreas had large herds of cattle and sheep.

The old Mission corridors were now the front porch of the house and the daughter of the household, about sixteen years of age, would come out during Estolano and Osvaldo's visit and sit and chat with the boys. Both courted her favor but so lavish and generous was she in her graciousness that neither of them ever knew which one stood the higher in her esteem.

Over the hills to the north of the Tapo Ranch some ten miles was the Camulos Ranch.* It belonged to Don Ignacio del Valle. His eldest son, Reginaldo del Valle had attended the Franciscan College with Estolano and Osvaldo. Reginaldo was now attending Santa Clara College and was home on vacation. Estolano and Osvaldo decided to pay Reginaldo a visit. On their arrival Reginaldo received them with open arms and at once ushered them into the presence of the rest of his family. His father was about sixty-five years old, while his mother was somewhat younger. He had one brother and three younger sisters. All accorded the visitors a warm welcome.

---

*This is the place made famous years later by Helen Hunt Jackson as the setting of her novel *Ramona.*

The house was a two-story adobe building, built in the form of a quadrangle. It faced the east. The front of the house was a solid wall. In the center was a large portal or doorway. Inside, the central part of the building was a beautiful pateo with many pretty flowers and shrubbery. A corridor extended all around the patio. Easy chairs and settees were everywhere about the corridors.

On the south side of the building was the kitchen and dining room. A large bedroom was at the end of the corridor. A stairway led to the upper story where a veranda extended all around the three sides of the house.

On the west side, opposite the entrance, was another large archway with double doors which led out into an outer corridor facing west and looking out over an almond orchard. On one side of the archway was a large *sala* or hall for dancing. The lower story of the right or north wing of the house was used for the servants and their families.

Soon the visitors were called to lunch. Don Ignacio himself did the serving. Noticing that Estolano was somewhat bashful he urged him to eat, saying with a hearty laugh:

"Young man, in this house we have only two meals a day, breakfast and supper. Eat plenty so you won't get hungry between meals."

That afternoon Reginaldo took the boys first through the warehouse. This was a large, two-story frame building. On the second floor all sorts of farm produce was stored. Among other things were large clusters of grapes, the bunches tied in pairs and hanging from nails driven into the stringers across the building. These were hung there in the process of making raisins. The visitors were urged to help themselves. These raisins were unlike any that Estolano had ever eaten before. They were very juicy and exceedingly sweet. Estolano recollected that the raisins upstairs at the Ranchito were never as sweet nor as juicy. He decided that those used at home were probably Mission grapes, while those at the Camulos Ranch were some improved variety.

After their walk through the warehouse the three young men saddled up their horses, and Reginaldo took his guests to look over the stock which was scattered for miles through the hills.

About four o'clock all were again called to the dining room. Estolano and Osvaldo begged to be excused, but Reginaldo insisted. So they went in for a cup of tea, following the old Spanish custom. Served with the tea were *tostados*. These are small biscuits in the shape of an abalone shell, but not quite so large. They are made with milk, eggs and sugar. They break open through the center and are served half toasted. Spread with butter, they are delicious. With the tea also came dishes of mixed nuts and raisins.

Although the boys were not hungry when they came down, still it was just impossible not to eat, everything was so tempting. Don Ignacio smiled and said cheerfully, with a twinkle in his eye:

"I saw you boys walking around so much this afternoon I was afraid you would get too weak before dinner. So I ordered this little bite especially for your benefit."

After tea the boys took a walk around on the south side of the house. Besides the many pretty flowers there were also several large shade trees. A nice graveled walk led to a large fountain some fifty or sixty feet from the corridors. The basin was about twelve feet in diameter and three feet deep. It held carp and gold fish. The water in the basin overflowed through the mouth of a lion and, running through the orchard, lost itself in the creek below.

About eight o'clock in the evening the family again assembled in the dining room for *Cena,* the main meal of the day. It was sumptuous. Estolano and Osvaldo were hardly prepared for this. At the school in Santa Barbara and at the Tapo Ranch only three meals a day were served. But the Camulos Ranch was an old Spanish household where five meals a day were observed, the fullest meal being the eight o'clock supper, as it had been at the Ranchito. But the old days were fast fading from Estolano's memory.

Later in the evening one of the little girls played the piano in the *Sala* and the younger brother and Reginaldo accompanied her on the violin. As Estolano listened to the entrancing dance music the thought stole through his mind how nice it would be if only Venturita were there to dance with him. Venturita was constantly uppermost in his mind. At the Tapo Ranch he had already composed some verses which he was hoping to present to her if he ever was in her home town again. He was quite pleased with the verses.

> *Venturita de mi vida*
> *Yo to adoro con afan*
> *No quisiera mas comida*
> *Que lo que tus labios dan.*
>
> *Ven pues a mis cansados brazos*
> *Quiero hablar y delirar contigo*
> *Quiero gozar tus debiles abrazos*
> *Besar tu sien y ser tu fiel amigo.*

Chapter XXXVIII

MONEY

ON THE RETURN of the boys to the Tapo Ranch, they found preparations under way for barbecuing a beef head for a celebration to be held the next morning. During their absence Don Francisco de la Guerra, Osvaldo's father, and his uncle, Don José Antonio, had come on a visit to Tapo.

A round hole had been dug in the ground about two feet in diameter and four feet deep. A hot fire of oak wood was burning in the bottom of the hole. Several good-sized rocks were being heated red hot. In the meantime the bull's head was being prepared. Green mint was stuffed into the ears, nose and mouth. The head was then carefully wrapped in a clean sack. When the fire in the pit had died out a layer of green mint was spread over the hot rocks. Then the beef head was dropped into the hole. Another layer of mint was added. Finally the hole was filled with dirt and tamped down tightly. The next morning the head was dug out. It was thoroughly cooked and was very inviting. With plenty of tortillas, Chili sauce, wine and coffee, Estolano thought the bull head breakfast was perfectly wonderful.

Don José Antonio was the eldest son of the de la Guerra family and was quite an old man. Although his pulse was shaky and his eyes were dim, yet after breakfast every morning he would have his horse, "Traga Leguas," saddled and brought around to the house. He would first take a spin through the woods and then coming back to the house would practice shooting with his revolver while riding his horse at full speed. He called his revolver his "Dragona," meaning dragoon. It was an old fashioned Navy of about forty-four calibre.

The housekeeper had a clothes line about sixty feet long back of the house. On it were stuck a great number of old fashioned wooden clothes pins. Don José Antonio would ride his horse on the run, first down one side of the clothes line, and then back up the other side firing as he went. He invariably would knock off two to four of the clothes pins out of six shots. Don José Antonio had been a Spanish soldier and was known as "El Capitan de la Guerra."

While the de la Guerras were visiting at the ranch, Estolano and Osvaldo decided one morning to go blackberrying. They saddled their horses, procured tin pails and started off up the creek. There was a trail through the woods. When about a mile from the house, they came to a small pond of water probably twenty feet across. In looking around, they discovered fresh bear tracks. It was a monster bear for the footprints were a foot long. The boys could also see where the bear had been wallowing in the pond and had splashed the water all around.

The tracks of the bear showed that it had gone into the willows in the direction of the blackberry patch towards which the boys were heading. Estolano had the more active horse, although it was not yet well broken to the bit. He rode ahead and Osvaldo followed. Being on the lookout both for berries and bears, Estolano noticed a nice little open space a short distance ahead. It was round like a circus ring and was probably a hundred and fifty feet in diameter. Surrounding it on all sides were blackberry vines.

There was a good-sized limb across the trail that led into the opening. It came just even with Estolano's breast. He bent down and rode under the limb. Just as he did so his horse gave a snort, reared up and turned to get away. Osvaldo hollered, "The bear!" and set out for home.

Estolano didn't get even to see the bear. His horse in its hurry to follow the other retreating horse plunged towards the limb over the trail. Estolano was almost knocked out of the saddle. But the colt being tender mouthed, he jerked him back on his haunches. Ducking his head down close to the horse's shoulder and closing his eyes he got safely through. When he looked for Osvaldo he was gone. He spurred his horse and soon caught up with him.

Estolano knew enough about bears to realize that the bear had probably gone as fast as it could in the opposite direction.

"You needn't be scared," he assured Osvaldo.

The two boys returned home and reported their bear story. Immediately the foreman and three vaqueros saddled up and got ready to go and get the bear. The cook insisted on going, too. The men got him a horse, and the five ranch hands with Estolano and Osvaldo in the lead started back up the creek on the hunt.

When the party reached the pond and the foreman saw the size of the bear tracks, he realized that it was indeed no common bear that they were going after. First he sent two men around the woods on the west side next to a low range of hills. Another man crossed the creek on the east side. He himself led the center of the attack. The cook was left behind and told to keep himself out of the way. Estolano and Osvaldo were allowed to follow, but were asked to keep behind at a distance.

The cook was holding his horse by the *mecate*. There was a sudden crashing through the woods. Something was coming! The cook's horse made a plunge and jerked loose. The cook jumped straight up into the air. His hands grasped the limb of a tree and there he hung. He kicked and screamed but nobody took any interest in him. All attention was centered on the bear.

— 245 —

The vaqueros in the meantime had chased the bear out into the open flat where there was room for them to exercise their horsemanship. The foreman was the first to throw his *riata*. One rope after another went around the bear's neck. But just as fast as a rope was thrown over his head, he would seize the rope with one of his paws and pull the horse and rider straight towards him until he had the rope slackened. Then as quick as lightning, with his other paw it would brush the rope off from around its neck. During all these maneuvers the bear kept working closer and closer to the woods. Finally with one jump it disappeared from sight.

"Well, boys," declared the foreman as the hunters were returning to the house, "that was certainly some bear!"

"By the way," asked Estolano, "where's the cook?"

All rode back. The cook was still hanging to the limb. His hands were so locked together from fright that the vaqueros had forcibly to pry his fingers loose. All the while the cook was bawling: "I'm not the least bit scared!"

On their return to the house Don Francisco, the owner of the ranch, simply laughed at his foreman and the vaqueros.

"I'll show you fellows how to catch a bear."

With that he ordered a beef killed and late that night had a front quarter hung in a tree along the trail where it was thought the bear traveled. Sometime during the night the bear took the bait.

The next day Don Francisco had a square hole dug about ten feet deep near the tree. Across this pit he ordered two poles placed. Upon these he had another large chunk of beef fastened. Then the whole thing was covered over with brush. This trap was set late in the evening.

The next morning Don Francisco sauntered out with a shotgun to get his bear. He took Estolano and Osvaldo along with him. Sure enough, down in the pit, helpless to get out, the bear was there waiting for him. Don Francisco gave the bear both barrels and laid him low. Then he had two men skin the bear and bring the hide to the house.

Don Francisco called the cook.

"There," he said in triumph, "look at that! There is the bear you were babbling so much about."

The skin was immense. It was at least eight feet long and five or six feet wide.

Estolano and Osvaldo spent most of the languid days of the long summer playing cards on the cots under the walnut trees or reading Spanish novels, of which Santiago had a great number. Much of their time they played a gambling game called "Stargo." It also went by the name of "Seven and a Half." They used beans for chips, twenty-five beans representing two bits.

A young man came up one day to the ranch on business. While he was waiting for Santiago, he came over to the cots to watch the boys play. Presently he asked if they would let him play, too. The boys consented and he sat down. After playing for a short time he remarked:

"Your cards are not much account."

Reaching into his pocket he brought out a nice clean deck that looked almost new.

Up to this point he had been losing almost constantly, but after the new deck was substituted he began to get the better of the two boys. Face cards were a half, and plain cards counted from one up to seven. Often the stranger would have a face card in the hole and then would unexpectedly turn up a seven spot for himself. That made seven and a half. Whenever the stranger made seven and a half the boys had to pay their bets double.

By noon the boys were out over a dollar each. After they had cashed in the stranger took them into his confidence. He admitted to them that he was a professional gambler. He offered them some advice.

"Never gamble with a stranger," he told them.

Then he explained to them his pack of cards. His was a special deck. Estolano and Osvaldo looked on in astonishment. The stranger could tell exactly what cards his opponents held in their hands. Each card had a special mark on the back which told him just what card it was!

Don Manuel Anguisola, whose sheep camp was up near the Tapo Ranch, was training a very pretty sorrel race horse to take to a race soon to be held at Hueneme. The purse was to be five hundred dollars. Anguisola had a nice half mile track fixed up at his sheep camp on which to train his racer. During the summer Osvaldo and Estolano, when tired of card playing and reading, would often come over from the Tapo to help exercise the horse.

The race was to be held the following Saturday. Hueneme was about fifty miles southwest of Tapo. When it was time to start Santiago and the boys were eager to travel. They all rode in the spring wagon. Two saddle horses were led behind. They stopped at Don Manuel Goldarcena's in the old Simi adobe for dinner. About sunset they came to an adobe ranch house where an elderly Don with a large family of girls lived. He had them stay for supper and then insisted on their remaining all night. The old man claimed that he had known Estolano's father, Don Manuel, as a young man, and he talked with Estolano for a long time. The three boys had already traveled twenty-five miles from Tapo that day and still had some thirty miles yet to go. They stayed over night and got an early start the next day, arriving at Hueneme about two in the afternoon.

The following morning after breakfast the three from Tapo watched the two race horses being exercised on the track. Anguisola's horse was certainly a beauty, a bright red sorrel with two white front feet. It weighed about one thousand pounds.

The owner of the other horse was an American who lived on a ranch just outside of Ventura. His horse was a blood red sorrel, solid color but rather ungainly. It was a larger horse than Anguisola's and weighed probably twelve hundred and fifty pounds.

The crowd that gathered in Hueneme that day to watch the race must have numbered in the neighborhood of two thousand people. Hueneme was only a small village along the sea coast. Where so many people came from was a mystery to Estolano. Anguisola's family, of course, was there. So were the Camarillos from Ventura. Raymundo Olivas from the Franciscan College and some of his family were also there.

Osvaldo and Estolano intended to sit their horses and watch the race. The track was only about a quarter of a mile from the center of the village.

After an early dinner at the hotel Estolano and Osvaldo were on the grounds at least an hour before the time for the race. They selected a good location where they had a full view of the finishing post. A few minutes before the time for the race to start a young American came riding close to the boys and was shouting:

"One hundred dollars to bet on the American horse."

He had several twenties in his hand and kept shaking them up and down tantalizingly. Estolano didn't like the fellow's insolence. Besides he felt that it was his duty to back the Anguisola horse, for he had exercised it so many times at the ranch. He knew it couldn't be beat. Hailing the chap, Estolano spoke up.

"I have no hundred dollars to bet, but I'll just go you a twenty on the Spanish horse."

"All right, my man, here you are."

Estolano dug down in his pocket and produced a twenty dollar gold piece. That was all the money he had except a dollar or two in change.

"Let your friend be the stake holder," the American said. At the same time he handed Osvaldo a twenty. Estolano did the same.

It was a tense moment. Estolano was wild for the race to start. After what seemed an interminable period the race was on. The little sorrel got the lead right from the start and kept it for better than half of the course. The big sorrel American horse began to gain. It caught up with the smaller horse. At the finish the Spanish horse was fully thirty feet behind.

Estolano was dumbfounded. The American came around to collect his bet and smiled with thanks as he walked away with Estolano's money. The possibility of the Spanish horse being beaten and his losing his twenty-dollar gold piece had never dawned on Estolano's mind.

The next morning Santiago drove the boys to Santa Barbara. Estolano and Osvaldo were glad to get back to familiar scenes. As it was a few days before the opening of the Franciscan College, Estolano remained the guest of Osvaldo at the Don Francisco de la Guerra home.

To Estolano's great surprise Venturita and her sister came to the de la Guerra home to call. They announced that they were attending the Sisters' Convent the following year. No one in the world could have been more greatly surprised than Estolano when he heard the news. He promptly seized the opportunity to ask Venturita if she and her sister would attend a little dinner party that evening at Estolano's favorite restaurant in town.

Estolano went later to the restaurant and arranged for a nice chicken dinner for a party of four. The restaurant owner agreed to give a fine lay-out for a dollar and a half a plate. Estolano and Osvaldo met the girls at Mrs. Kahn's. They had a private dining room at the restaurant and a splendid dinner was served in courses. Venturita was even more charming than at home, and Estolano was feeling very proud of himself as a host.

Estolano understood that champagne was tasty and proper at high-toned dinners. As he wanted to make the best impression possible on Venturita, he ordered a bottle. He knew that champagne was good tasting, but he had very little idea of the cost. The party finished the first bottle, then another and another. Three bottles in all. Estolano helped Venturita with her last glass which she had tried to decline.

All enjoyed the dinner splendidly. When the party was ready to leave Estolano rushed up to the desk to pay the bill. In utter abandon he slammed down a ten dollar gold piece on the counter and called for the amount of the dinner.

The proprietor looked at the ten dollar gold piece for a moment and then said quietly:

"Your bill is twenty-two fifty."

Estolano thought he would sink straight through the floor. Besides, the ten dollar gold piece was all the money he had.

"But," stammered Estolano, recovering himself, "I thought the dinner was to be six dollars."

The proprietor explained courteously:

"Six dollars for the dinner. Fifteen dollars for the champagne. A dollar and a half for extras."

Estolano looked beseachingly at Osvaldo.

"I haven't but a dollar!"

Realizing Estolano's predicament, the restaurant man picked up Estolano's ten dollar gold piece and dropping it in the till, smiled graciously:

"I'll give you until tomorrow noon to pay the balance!"

Estolano felt later, however, that he was amply repaid for all his embarrassment. On the way to the Convent Venturita confided:

"Estolano, you are a perfect host. I'm so glad I'm going to be in Santa Barbara this year."

As they neared the Convent, they stole their first kiss. It made Estolano's blood tingle. All the rest of the way he felt like he was walking on air.

San Juan Mission Bells 1870

Chapter XXXIX

OYSTERS AND KISSES

A WEEK OR SO before commencement Anatolio and Lupe Anzar arrived in Santa Barbara. With them was Patrocinio, Estolano's brother. All three were on their way to Los Angeles. Patrocinio and Anatolio wanted to see their guardian, Dr. MacDougall, and get money from him to open up a livery stable business for themselves on Market Street in San Francisco. Lupe was already in business for himself and was running a livery stable on Spring Street in Los Angeles.

As soon as commencement was over, Estolano was on his way for his promised visit with Lupe. The stage for Los Angeles left Santa Barbara about two or three o'clock in the afternoon. A stop for supper was made at the Santa Clara Hotel in Ventura. Only one change of horses had been made between Santa Barbara and Ventura. Here a second change of horses was made, and the stage left Ventura at eight o'clock in the evening. It was another sleepless night for Estolano. But the road was not nearly so rough as it had been between San Juan Bautista and Santa Barbara four years before.

About five o'clock in the morning the stage reached the foot of the San Marcos Grade across the Simi Valley. Here there was a stage station and eating house. The breakfast was very fair. They even served hot cakes and honey. Estolano had always been very fond of honey but this was black and had a peculiar taste. Estolano was inquisitive and upon inquiry found the stage station keeper had about two hundred hives of bees at the station and that the honey was made from sunflowers.

After changing horses three times that forenoon, the stage arrived in Los Angeles a little before noon. All the passengers stopped at the Pico House, then the bon-ton hotel in Los Angeles. It had been built by Don Pio Pico, the last Mexican Governor of California. The hotel was located on Spring Street. Main and Spring were the leading business streets of Los Angeles, like Kearny and Montgomery were in San Francisco at the time. The Pico House was four stories high and was considered a fine piece of architecture. Estolano was given a room on the third floor.

Estolano had no difficulty in finding Lupe. He was running a livery stable just across the Plaza from the hotel. After dinner Lupe hitched up a single buggy and he and Estolano drove out along San Pedro Avenue to visit Dr. MacDougall, whose residence was about a mile south of the city. Later they took a ride all over town. There may have been twenty-five hundred inhabitants at the time. The principal streets were Spring, Main, San Pedro and Los Angeles.

Lupe's stable was known as the Plaza Livery. The main entrance fronted on Spring Street. There was a long basement the whole length of the stable and all the livery horses were kept down there. Only the vehicles were kept on the first floor. He had a fine assortment of carriages, top and open buggies and barouches. He also had closed coaches and cabs, with drivers, if desired.

Lupe was a natural-born horseman. He knew horses, he liked them and he took the very best care of them. He had a large enclosure across the alley back of the stable. Here the horses were turned loose every day, three or four at a time, to exercise themselves. Lupe had a large pile of clean sand in one corner of the lot especially for them to roll in.

It was quite fashionable at this time for young ladies to ride horseback. On Sundays groups of from two to six would call at the stable for horses to ride. All used sidesaddles. It was quite against the social order and considered very unladylike for a girl to ride a horse astride like a man. With their long riding habits and plumed headgear and sitting erect on spirited, prancing horses, these fine-looking young ladies were a thrilling sight to Estolano as they paraded along the city's thoroughfares.

Ysidro German and his brother, Felipe, from San Juan Bautista, arrived in Los Angeles driving a bunch of saddle and buggy horses for Lupe's stable. These horses had been left in a field at the edge of town. Lupe and Estolano got horses and rode out with Ysidro to look over the condition of the stock. Lupe was well satisfied. Among the horses was a span of iron gray mares, so much alike in color, size and action, that only the shrewdest horseman could tell them apart. They were both five minute horses. Lupe had purchased them in San Juan for six hundred dollars. There was also a young sorrel mare—a racer and a perfect beauty. Lupe caught up the two grays and the sorrel and led them down to the livery stable. The next day room was made for the other saddle horses.

Sunday morning Lupe had this newly arrived trotting team of grays hitched up to a light top buggy. The young men sallied forth in the direction of the nearest beach then called the "William Tell," about ten miles distant. The road was perfectly level and ran most of the way through marshy land. The road was packed hard and made a splendid trotting ground. Lupe let the little team out for all they were worth. The horses certainly could make time. They overtook and passed six or eight other vehicles.

"William Tell" was a pretty beach. Many pot-holes in the sand were filled with clear, clean salt water. People unable to swim took advantage of these dipping holes to take their ocean baths. Some of the holes were large enough for two or three people to get in them at the same time.

There was only one building at the beach. It was prettily built in imitation of a Swiss chateau. On one side was a row of little rooms where people could change their clothes, putting on bathing suits which were kept for rent at the chateau. All sorts of refreshments were sold, including soft drinks. Lupe and Estolano walked around the beach for a time, then had a drink of lemonade and finally took the road back to Los Angeles.

One morning Lupe had the little sorrel mare saddled up with an English riding saddle and asked Estolano to get on and ride her for exercise. Estolano was a good rider and was always ready to ride a pretty horse. However, he had never ridden on an English saddle. To him it was no saddle at all. He would much rather have preferred to ride bareback.

"Go down to the river bed and try her a spurt," said Lupe.

Straight to the river Estolano went. It was not long before he came upon a nice level stretch where the sand was packed hard. He followed this for about three hundred yards, then turned the horse around. He fixed himself properly in the saddle, only the tips of his toes touching the stirrups. Taking hold of the horse's long mane with his right hand he hollered "Go!" The little horse certainly knew the call. With a jump of at least fifteen feet she shot forward like an arrow out of a bow. Had not Estolano been prepared for it, he would have been left sitting behind.

The racer ran the distance Estolano had selected. Then checking her by degrees, he soothed her excitement by talking gently to her. He walked her along the river until she was cooled down again to normal.

Estolano decided to go back to town by way of the Mexican Quarter on the north side. It was known as Sonora Town. Estolano felt that he was a great spectacle to the people whom he passed. The little horse carried herself like an Arab steed, with arched neck and a fancy forward step.

Estolano kept to the right side of the street as he rode through Sonora Town. He gazed here and there at the low adobe houses. From the looks of them he surmised that this may have been the original part of Los Angeles. While absorbed in this thought, suddenly his horse shied, making a jump forward and sideways. This caught Estolano unawares and nearly proved his upsetting. He grabbed for the saddle horn. But there was no saddle horn. At the same time he found that since there was no cantle or back to this saddle that he was sitting behind the saddle instead of on it. It was only by his holding firmly to the reins that he prevented himself from being left completely behind on the ground.

The cause of the horse's fright was a little squalling baby sprawled in front of a miserable little shack. Estolano looked at the woman who came rushing to pick up the baby. The woman looked at Estolano. Both recognized each other simultaneously. It was Doña Desideria de Madrano, who with her husband, Felipe, had lived at the Ranchito for a number of years.

While visiting Doña Desiderata during the afternoon, Estolano learned that there was going to be a dance in Sonora Town that night. At Desideria's house he also met a little neighbor of hers, a young girl of about sixteen. She was a pretty brunette. She made Estolano promise to attend the dance and it was understood between them that they were to have many dances together.

Lupe and Estolano attended the party, merely a home affair. But the music was good and there were many beautiful señoritas. Estolano's little friend was there of course, in a neat black silk dress with many flounces. She kept her promise to Estolano and they had many dances together. Later he had the pleasure of walking home with Carmelita, for that was her name. It was only about three blocks from the dance to her home. But the way was all too short for Estolano. He parted from her feeling rather disconsolate, for he was leaving Los Angeles the next day and he realized that he would never see her again.

Lupe and Estolano the next morning were walking through the billiard hall in the Pico House. Sitting in a large chair, all alone, was a very distinguished looking elderly man. He was large and tall. His rather dark features were made all the more prominent by a massive head of white hair and heavy snowy white beard. Lupe walked up to him and shook hands, then introduced Estolano. It was Don Pio Pico himself, who in early days had been twice the Mexican Governor of California. Estolano doffed his hat and shook hands.

Don Pio bade the young men sit along side of him. He asked Estolano his age and who his father was. When Estolano told him he grasped Estolano's hand and said: "Young man, I am very glad to meet you. Your father and I were very good friends." Lupe and Estolano visited with the old governor for almost an hour.

Lupe's room in the Pico House was beyond Estolano's on the north side of the hallway. As they were going up to their rooms for Estolano to check out, the door of the room just next to Estolano's was standing slightly ajar. Estolano peered in. The sight almost overpowered him. There lying at full length on the carpet was a man in his shirt sleeves. His clothes were covered with blood. His throat was cut from ear to ear!

Estolano called to Lupe who came running back. Seeing the terrible sight, he ran down stairs in double quick time and informed the hotel office. The coroner was sent for. In no time at all fully a dozen men were in the room with Estolano. They looked around the room and found a bloody razor lying along side of the body. They touched nothing.

It was not long until the coroner arrived. He officially pronounced the man dead. Estolano could not help but smile slightly. Anyone seeing the yawning gash in the man's throat couldn't help but know the man was dead. A spring wagon was immediately procured and the body taken away.

Estolano later that afternoon took the train for Wilmington. The distance was about thirty miles from Los Angeles. There he went aboard a steamer for San Francisco and four days later entered the Golden Gate.

That evening Estolano's brother, Patrocinio, and Helen, his bride of only a few weeks, invited Estalano to attend the California Theater where "Aladdin, or the Wonderful Lamp" was being given. Christine Nielson was the prima donna. She was dressed as a boy and represented Aladdin. When lost in the beautiful garden she sang "Sweet Spirit, Hear My Prayer." Many a tear was wiped from the eyes of those in the audience.

Saturday Estolano and his sister-in-law, Helen, decided to visit Woodward's Garden. This amusement park was the most popular resort in the city. It was out near Mission Dolores. The park had a great menagerie and aquarium, an aviary, a Palace of Arts and Antiques, much shrubbery and all sorts of punching and lifting machines. There was a fine large auditorium where vaudeville and pantomimes were given. A brass band furnished the music. In addition to all these attractions there was a large dining room on the second floor, all enclosed in glass, where refreshments of all kinds were served.

On the way to the park Estolano and Helen stopped to visit with some friends. A Miss Smith was invited to accompany them. She was a nice-looking girl of about eighteen and very vivacious. They took in everything there was to see, even the punching machines. Then they visited the Auditorium in time to see the performance and listen to the band. After this Estolano proposed that they have a bite to eat. He asked Helen to do the ordering. She ordered half a dozen raw oysters for each of them. Estolano added a bottle of white Sauterne wine.

Estolano had never eaten a fresh oyster in his life. He carefully fixed his the same way he saw the ladies fixing theirs, a little lemon juice, salt and pepper and tomato ketchup. The looks of the raw oysters on his plate did not in any way sharpen his desire to swallow one.

Estolano helped the girls to wine, then himself. They drank and then all started in on the oysters. Estolano put an oyster in his mouth, thinking that by making a desperate effort he could swallow it. But the thing simply wouldn't go down. Surreptitiously he wiped the oyster out of his mouth with his napkin.

Helen was watching and she laughed at him. He felt very much abashed for soon both the ladies were poking fun at him. Finally Miss Smith said banteringly:

"If you will swallow an oyster I will give you a kiss when we get home."

Estolano looked at her pretty mouth. He decided that he would try anything for even one sweet kiss. He took up another oyster, closed his eyes, and with a great effort gulped it down. Taking a sip of wine he said boldly:

"For a second kiss I'll swallow another one."

The young girl opposite him agreed and another oyster followed the first one. He kept on bargaining until he had swallowed all five oysters on his plate.

"At this rate of pay," declared Estolano smiling, "I would keep on swallowing oysters all day long."

Miss Smith acknowledged the compliment with one of her prettiest smiles.

The party did not linger long in the park after their oyster repast. On their way home Estolano sat between the two ladies and kept remarking how slowly the street car was traveling.

Finally they arrived at Miss Smith's home. Her mother and her younger sister had gone to the matinee. Helen on her part hastened away in order to.get supper for her husband.

Miss Smith was all eagerness to pay her debt and Estolano got his five kisses. Still unsatisfied, he demanded a sixth for the oyster he hadn't eaten!

Chapter XXXX

COMMENCEMENT

COMMENCEMENT is a beginning, not an ending.

For Estolano, as for all who are graduating, it was a time of turmoil. He now found himself no longer an onlooker, but one of the principals. Instead of a happy time, it was one of the utmost confusion. His mind was like a whirlwind, blowing in all directions. He felt himself standing as it were on a precipice, abandoned by all. Conduct was no longer mapped out for him to follow. From now on he must make his own decisions in life.

-Ever since his visit to Bernardo at the Quien Sabe sheep camp, when his nephew tried to induce him to become a sheep man, Estolano had begun to think seriously about the future. He suddenly realized that college life could not go on forever. It began to dawn on him that there were things far more important in life than hunting and dancing. The question what his future life was to be had been plaguing him ever since. By now Estolano had made up his mind definitely as to what he hoped to be. He was equally certain that he wanted to be neither a business man nor a rancher.

Just before commencement week Estolano had received a letter from his guardian, directing him to come down to Los Angeles immediately after the commencement exercises. Dr. MacDougall casually mentioned that he and Mrs. MacDougall would be celebrating their wedding anniversary, and they wanted Lupe and Estolano to be present.

Came Commencement. The entire school was up in the air with excitement. Fifteen of their number would never be back again. Fifteen this year were to receive their diplomas and pass out into the world. The student body *en masse* trudged down town and into the Lobero Theater. Judge McGuire and Judge de la Guerra, together with Father O'Keefe, were the committee in charge. There were plays, declamations and music. Fifteen boys each received a diploma. Among them was Don Estolano, now a young man of nineteen. All that Estolano could remember of the exciting occasion was a remark by one of the Judges, as he gave out the diplomas, something about Spanish boys whose fathers had lost California and American boys whose fathers had seized a new state for the Union. All were ready to set out together in the race for life, all on an equal footing and with an even start. None were any longer Spanish. All were Americans!

On arriving in Los Angeles, Estolano went at once to Lupe and together they drove out to the house of Estolano's guardian. The Mayor's residence, Dr. MacDougall's home, was a large two-story building. There were big double parlors. A large number of friends of the mayor and of the family were already seated in the front parlor when Estolano and Lupe arrived. Dr. MacDougall introduced them to all, then had the two boys take seats in the back parlor where the young people of the party were gathered. In the mayor's family there were two girls, Bella, about seventeen, and Laura, fifteen. Both were good-looking and attractive. In the front parlor were the married people, some young and some past middle age. A soloist from time to time during the evening sang Spanish and English ballads.

Frequently a colored butler circulated through the assemblage carrying a tray filled with glasses of champagne. Laura and Estolano occupied a little settee at the right hand side of the archway connecting the two parlors. Invariably they were the first of the young people to be served. Laura drank her second glass very bravely, but when it came to the third she invited Estolano to share it with her. Estolano was only too glad to sip from her glass for he felt that it showed that she liked him. He was also pleased to help her drain her glass, for he was finding that he liked champagne. It didn't dawn on him that the mild, watery stuff could pack such a wallop. At every turn, when they were served Estolano, after drinking his own, kept helping Laura with hers. Laura would merely touch her glass to her lips and then with a sly glance and smile pass it over to him. Estolano felt very manly helping her. No one kept count of how many times the butler came into the room with more champagne. All that Estolano remembered was that he was feeling very jolly and never refused another glass.

About eleven o'clock supper was announced. The guests marched through the front parlor and down the hallway to the dining room. Laura and Estolano waited in line for Lupe and Bella. They all started marching out together, but on reaching the hall Estolano began to feel very queer.

"I'm so dizzy," whispered Estolano to Lupe. Then he added soon after: "My legs are just like rubber. I don't think I better try to go into the dining room."

The stairway was just beside him. Lupe asked the girls to wait where they were. The two boys went upstairs. Lupe had often stayed over night at the MacDougall home.

"I think you better show me where we are to sleep tonight," said Estolano.

"You can take either bed you wish," announced Lupe as the two entered the bedroom where he and Estolano were to sleep. There were two beds in the room. Estolano chose the one next to the window.

Estolano undressed and managed to get into bed. To his astonishment the moment he closed his eyes the bedstead began whirling around and around like a spinning top. He half way thought that someone was playing a trick on him. He sat bolt upright and looked out the window. At once the bed stopped revolving. It was a bright, clear night and quite light outside. He lay down again. Immediately the bed began spinning. Again he sat up. By this time spinning around so much had made him deathly sick to his stomach.

Invariably every time he lay back in bed and closed his eyes the bed would start its pranks again. His only relief was to sit up and look out the window. He began to think that he would have to sit up all night. He had a notion to jump out of the window. Finally after about an hour, from sheer exhaustion, lying down and getting up, he fell asleep.

Estolano never heard Lupe when he came to bed. Nor did he once wake up until the sun was shining in the window. Lupe and he got up and went down to the breakfast table together. Estolano felt so chagrined. But everyone greeted the boys affiably, as though nothing had happened. The Doctor sat at the head of the table. His wife was busy trying to make everyone feel welcome and perfectly at ease. Estolano couldn't help but notice, however, that the two girls were having difficulty in keeping from laughing.

Estolano hoped that no one would bring up the unpleasantness of the evening before. But as the Doctor arose from the table he said to Estolano:

"I want to have a talk with you in my study when you are at leisure."

Estolano was deeply mortified. Becoming intoxicated at the Doctor's wedding anniversary! He resolved never again to drink champagne.

"Be seated, Estolano," directed the Doctor as he pointed out a seat directly in front of the large desk behind which the tall Scotchman was sitting.

"The reason why I have sent for you to come to me is so that I can have a serious talk with you. What do you intend to do in life?"

Estolano was so taken aback that he was speechless. He simply sat there open-mouthed.

"Now, Estolano," continued his guardian, "if you want to start up in business for yourself you have the means to do so. Lupe is doing well here in Los Angeles in his livery business."

After a pause as if to let the matter sink in he went on.

"Your brother, Patrocinio, is getting along first rate in San Francisco."

The Doctor finally looked up from his desk.

"Of course, Estolano, I've always had you in the back of my head as my superintendent of my ranches. You are especially fitted for such a position. Would you care to take over their management?"

Now that Estolano discovered that the Doctor was not going to take him to task for the past but was looking forward into the future he suddenly grew bold.

"Doctor, I would far rather take over your medical practice."

Doctor MacDougall instantly resented Estolano's insolence. He was plainly annoyed. He quickly decided that Estolano was still only a boy mentally.

"Don't you understand, Estolano, that in order for you to do that you would have to be a medical doctor?"

"That's what I would like to be."

His guardian looked at Estolano in amazement. "You a doctor!"

Estolano remained stupidly silent for want of words. It took Dr. MacDougall several minutes to control his surprise.

"Well," he finally exploded, "I never thought of you as wanting to become a doctor!"

Dr. MacDougall could see that Estolano was deadly in earnest.

"Funny, isn't it," mused his guardian, "that I never thought of such a thing before."

The doctor looked at Estolano critically as though he were diagnosing a patient.

"Plagued if I don't think you would make a splendid doctor!"

After a pause he went on. "Your Aunt Pilar is one of the best midwives in California. I'll take off my hat to her in respect any day."

"And," continued the doctor, "I never had occasion to re-set a bone that your brother—what was his name—the 'Bone Setter' handled."

The doctor was still reminiscent. "Do you remember the time your father's cousin was found murdered at the Ranchito gate. You helped me make the *post mortem*. I thought at that time that you sure were good for nothing but the law."

Looking at the timid but determined face of Estolano, the doctor finally broke out in a smile.

"Why haven't you ever told me this before? I could have had you in my office every summer vacation. You would have been well on your way to becoming a doctor already."

Estolano remained silent as his guardian pondered. At last, looking up, the doctor spoke with decision.

"I'll be very happy to recommend you for admission to my University."

"The University of Glasgow is a great medical school.

"You will enjoy your stay in Europe. There is so much to see and to experience.

"When you have your diploma and have served your internship I'll be most happy to have you associated with me here in Los Angeles."

The doctor paused.

"Estolano, I thoroughly approve of your choice in life. There is always a place in this world for a good doctor."

Rushing out into the dining room where Lupe and the rest of the family were anxiously awaiting the outcome of Estolano's reprimand, the Doctor, dragging the embarrassed Estolano with him, announced triumphantly:

"Estolano has just told me his decision. Estolano is to be my future partner. He is going to study medicine in Scotland. I give you—and he beamed in admiration on his ward—

'Doctor Estolano Larios!"

The San Juan Mission Sun Dial